CALIFORNIA INTEGRATE

elevate science

AUTHORS

You're an author!

As you write in this science book, your answers and personal discoveries will be recorded for you to keep, making this book unique to you. That is why you are one of the primary authors of this book.

In the space below, print your name, school, town, and state. Then write a short autobiography that includes your interests and accomplishments.

YOUR NAME ....

SCHOOL ....

TOWN, STATE ....

AUTOBIOGRAPHY ....

Savvas Learning Company LLC, 15 East Midland Avenue, Paramus, NJ 07652

Cover: The cover shows a Joshua tree and a Joshua tree bloom in Joshua Tree National Park. Many interesting rock formations are also found in the park. In the sky a star factory of more than 800,000 stars is being born. FCVR: Casey Kiernan/Moment/Getty Images, Meganopierson/Shutterstock, Zoonar GmbH/Alamy Stock Photo, Stocktrek Images, Inc./Alamy Stock Photo; BCVR: Marinello/DigitalVision Vectors/Getty Images.

Attributions of third party content appear on page 188, which constitutes an extension of this copyright page.

ISBN-13: 978-1-418-31041-7
ISBN-10: 1-418-31041-7
4 21

Program Authors

ZIPPORAH MILLER, Ed.D.
Coordinator for K-12 Science Programs, Anne Arundel County Public Schools
Dr. Zipporah Miller currently serves as the Senior Manager for Organizational Learning with the Anne Arundel County Public School System. Prior to that she served as the K-12 Coordinator for science in Anne Arundel County. She conducts national training to science stakeholders on the Next Generation Science Standards. Dr. Miller also served as the Associate Executive Director for Professional Development Programs and conferences at the National Science Teachers Association (NSTA) and served as a reviewer during the development of Next Generation Science Standards. Dr. Miller holds a doctoral degree from the University of Maryland College Park, a master's degree in school administration and supervision from Bowie State University and a bachelor's degree from Chadron State College.

MICHAEL J. PADILLA, Ph.D.
Professor Emeritus, Eugene P. Moore School of Education, Clemson University, Clemson, South Carolina
Michael J. Padilla taught science in middle and secondary schools, has more than 30 years of experience educating middle-school science teachers, and served as one of the writers of the 1996 U.S. National Science Education Standards. In recent years Mike has focused on teaching science to English Language Learners. His extensive experience as Principal Investigator on numerous National Science Foundation and U.S. Department of Education grants resulted in more than $35 million in funding to improve science education. He served as president of the National Science Teachers Association, the world's largest science teaching organization, in 2005–6.

MICHAEL E. WYSESSION, Ph.D
Professor of Earth and Planetary Sciences, Washington University, St. Louis, Missouri
Author of more than 100 science and science education publications, Dr. Wysession was awarded the prestigious National Science Foundation Presidential Faculty Fellowship and Packard Foundation Fellowship for his research in geophysics, primarily focused on using seismic tomography to determine the forces driving plate tectonics. Dr. Wysession is also a leader in geoscience literacy and education; he is the chair of the Earth Science Literacy Initiative, the author of several popular video lectures on geology in the *Great Courses* series, and a lead writer of the *Next Generation Science Standards**.

---

*Next Generation Science Standards is a registered trademark of WestEd. Neither WestEd nor the lead states and partners that developed the Next Generation Science Standards were involved in the production of this product, and do not endorse it. NGSS Lead States. 2013. *Next Generation Science Standards: For States, By States.* Washington, DC: The National Academies Press.

REVIEWERS

Program Consultants

Carol Baker
Science Curriculum

Dr. Carol K. Baker is superintendent for Lyons Elementary K-8 School District in Lyons, Illinois. Prior to this, she was Director of Curriculum for Science and Music in Oak Lawn, Illinois. Before this she taught Physics and Earth Science for 18 years. In the recent past, Dr. Baker also wrote assessment questions for ACT (EXPLORE and PLAN), was elected president of the Illinois Science Teachers Association from 2011–2013, and served as a member of the Museum of Science and Industry (Chicago) advisory board. She is a writer of the Next Generation Science Standards. Dr. Baker received her B.S. in Physics and a science teaching certification. She completed her master's of Educational Administration (K-12) and earned her doctorate in Educational Leadership.

Jim Cummins
ELL

Dr. Cummins's research focuses on literacy development in multilingual schools and the role technology plays in learning across the curriculum. *Elevate Science* incorporates research-based principles for integrating language with the teaching of academic content based on Dr. Cummins's work.

Elfrieda Hiebert
Literacy

Dr. Hiebert, a former primary-school teacher, is President and CEO of TextProject, a non-profit aimed at providing open-access resources for instruction of beginning and struggling readers, She is also a research associate at the University of California Santa Cruz. Her research addresses how fluency, vocabulary, and knowledge can be fostered through appropriate texts, and her contributions have been recognized through awards such as the Oscar Causey Award for Outstanding Contributions to Reading Research (Literacy Research Association, 2015), Research to Practice award (American Educational Research Association, 2013), and the William S. Gray Citation of Merit Award for Outstanding Contributions to Reading Research (International Reading Association, 2008).

Content Reviewers

Alex Blom, Ph.D.
Associate Professor
Department Of Physical Sciences
Alverno College
Milwaukee, Wisconsin

Joy Branlund, Ph.D.
Department of Physical Science
Southwestern Illinois College
Granite City, Illinois

Judy Calhoun
Associate Professor
Physical Sciences
Alverno College
Milwaukee, Wisconsin

Stefan Debbert
Associate Professor of Chemistry
Lawrence University
Appleton, Wisconsin

Diane Doser
Professor
Department of Geological Sciences
University of Texas at El Paso
El Paso, Texas

Rick Duhrkopf, Ph.D.
Department of Biology
Baylor University
Waco, Texas

Jennifer Liang
University of Minnesota Duluth
Duluth, Minnesota

Heather Mernitz, Ph.D.
Associate Professor of Physical Sciences
Alverno College
Milwaukee, Wisconsin

Joseph McCullough, Ph.D.
Cabrillo College
Aptos, California

Katie M. Nemeth, Ph.D.
Assistant Professor
College of Science and Engineering
University of Minnesota Duluth
Duluth, Minnesota

Maik Pertermann
Department of Geology
Western Wyoming Community College
Rock Springs, Wyoming

Scott Rochette
Department of the Earth Sciences
The College at Brockport State University of New York
Brockport, New York

David Schuster
Washington University in St Louis
St. Louis, Missouri

Shannon Stevenson
Department of Biology
University of Minnesota Duluth
Duluth, Minnesota

Paul Stoddard, Ph.D.
Department of Geology and Environmental Geosciences
Northern Illinois University
DeKalb, Illinois

Nancy Taylor
American Public University
Charles Town, West Virginia

Teacher Reviewers

Rita Armstrong
Los Cerritos Middle School
Thousand Oaks, California

Tyler C. Britt, Ed.S.
Curriculum & Instructional Practice Coordinator
Raytown Quality Schools
Raytown, Missouri

Holly Bowser
Barstow High School
Barstow, California

David Budai
Coachella Valley Unified School District
Coachella, California

A. Colleen Campos
Grandview High School
Aurora, Colorado

Jodi DeRoos
Mojave River Academy
Colton, California

Colleen Duncan
Moore Middle School
Redlands, California

Nicole Hawke
Westside Elementary
Thermal, California

Margaret Henry
Lebanon Junior High School
Lebanon, Ohio

Ashley Humphrey
Riverside Preparatory Elementary
Oro Grande, California

Adrianne Kilzer
Riverside Preparatory Elementary
Oro Grande, California

Danielle King
Barstow Unified School District
Barstow, California

Kathryn Kooyman
Riverside Preparatory Elementary
Oro Grande, California

Esther Leonard M.Ed. and L.M.T.
Gifted and Talented Implementation Specialist
San Antonio Independent School District
San Antonio, Texas

Diana M. Maiorca, M.Ed.
Los Cerritos Middle School
Thousand Oaks, California

Kevin J. Maser, Ed.D.
H. Frank Carey Jr/Sr High School
Franklin Square, New York

Corey Mayle
Brogden Middle School
Durham, North Carolina

Keith McCarthy
George Washington Middle School
Wayne, New Jersey

Rudolph Patterson
Cobalt Institute of Math and Science
Victorville, California

Yolanda O. Peña
John F. Kennedy Junior High School
West Valley City, Utah

Stacey Phelps
Mojave River Academy
Oro Grande, California

Susan Pierce
Bryn Mawr Elementary
Redlands Unified School District
Redlands, California

Cristina Ramos
Mentone Elementary School
Redlands Unified School District
Mentone, California

Mary Regis
Franklin Elementary School
Redlands, California

Bryna Selig
Gaithersburg Middle School
Gaithersburg, Maryland

Pat (Patricia) Shane, Ph.D.
STEM & ELA Education Consultant
Chapel Hill, North Carolina

Elena Valencia
Coral Mountain Academy
Coachella, California

Janelle Vecchio
Mission Elementary School
Redlands, California

Brittney Wells
Riverside Preparatory Elementary
Oro Grande, California

Kristina Williams
Sequoia Middle School
Newbury Park, California

Safety Reviewers

Douglas Mandt, M.S.
Science Education Consultant
Edgewood, Washington

Juliana Textley, Ph.D.
Author, NSTA books on school science safety
Adjunct Professor
Lesley University
Cambridge, Massachusetts

California Spotlight
Instructional Segment 4
TOPICS 8–10

California Floristic Province

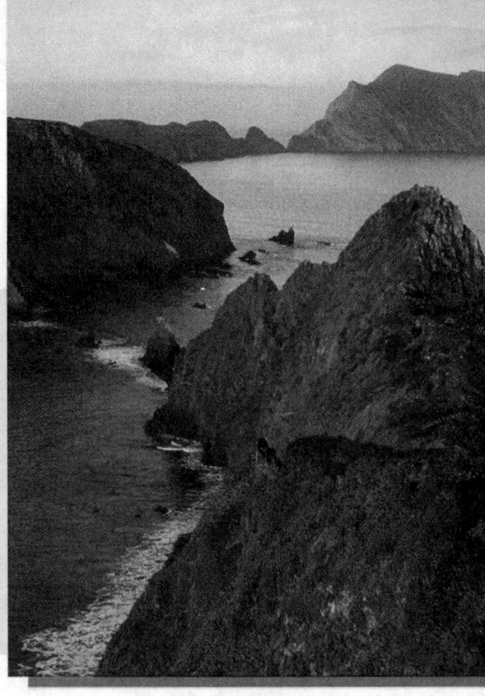

TOPIC 8

Plate Tectonics 8

Investigative Phenomenon Why is it important to analyze and interpret data to provide evidence for past plate motions?

 MS-ESS2-2, MS-ESS2-3, MS-ESS3-2, EP&CIb

HANDS-ON LABS

- Connect
- Investigate
- Demonstrate

TOPIC 9 Earth's Surface Systems

Investigative Phenomenon What evidence is there to explain how geoscience processes have changed Earth's surface over time?

MS-ESS2-2, MS-ESS3-1, MS-ESS3-2, EP&CIc, EP&CIIIa, EP&CIIIb

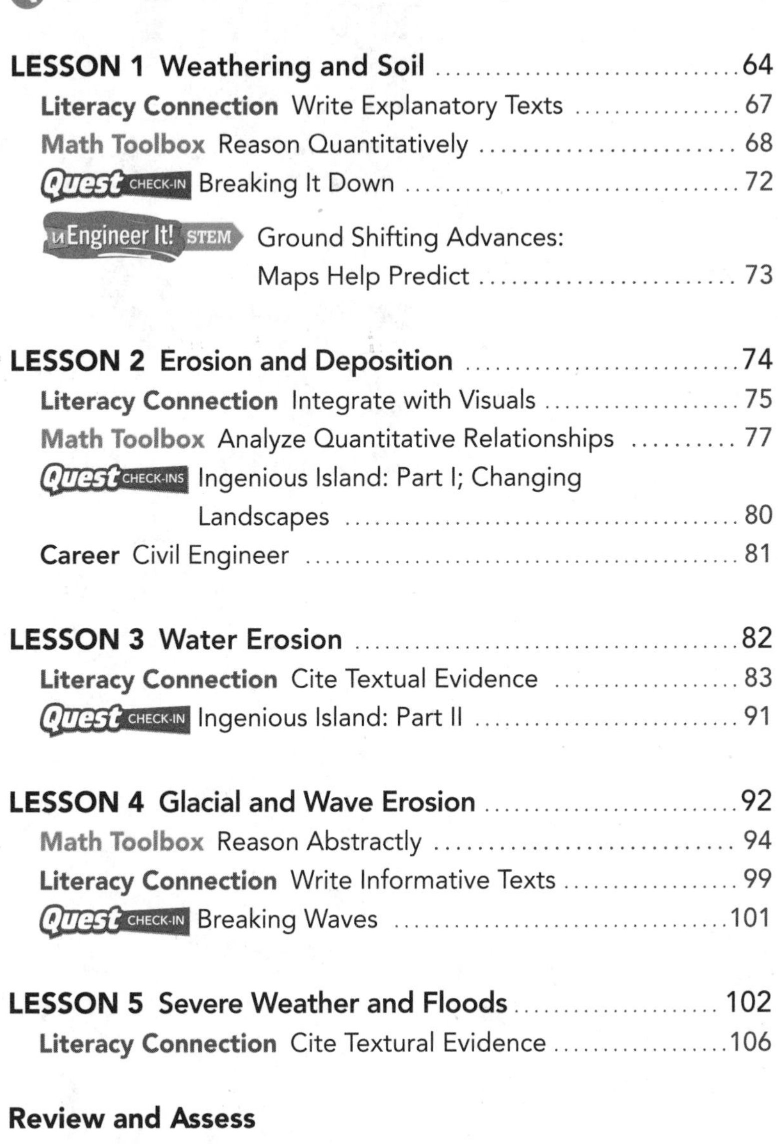

uConnect

uInvestigate

uDemonstrate

TOPIC 10

Populations, Communities, and Ecosystems 118

 MS-LS2-1, MS-LS2-2, MS-LS2-3, MS-LS2-4, MS-LS2-5, EP&CIc, EP&CIIb, EP&CIIIa, EP&CIIIb, EP&CIIIc, EP&CIVc, EP&CVa

California Spotlight

California Floristic Province

Go to SavvasRealize.com to access your digital course.

Elevate Science combines the best science narrative with a robust online program. Throughout the lessons, digital support is presented at point of use to enhance your learning experience.

Online Resources

Savvas Realize™ is your online science class. This digital-learning environment includes:

- Student eTEXT
- Instructor eTEXT
- Project-Based Learning
- Virtual Labs
- Interactivities
- Videos
- Assessments
- Study Tools
- and more!

Digital Features

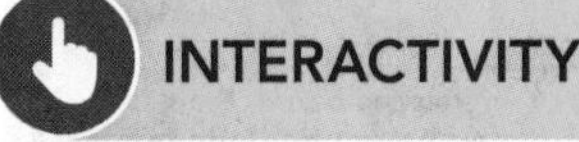

Keep an eye out for these **icons**, which indicate the different ways your textbook is enhanced online.

Digital activities are located throughout the narrative to deepen your understanding of scientific concepts.

Interpret models of relationships in various ecosystems.

Elevate your thinking!

California Elevate Science takes science to a whole new level and lets you take ownership of your learning. Explore science in the world around you. Investigate how things work. Think critically and solve problems! *California Elevate Science* helps you think like a scientist, so you're ready for a world of discoveries.

Exploring California

California spotlights explore California phenomena. Topic Quests help connect lesson concepts together and reflect 3-dimensional learning.

- Science concepts organized around phenomena
- Topics weave together 3-D learning
- Engineering focused on solving problems and improving designs

California Spotlight
Instructional Segment 2

Before the Topics
Identify the Problem

California Flood Management

Phenomenon In February of 2017, workers at the Orov

Quest KICKOFF

How can you use solids, liquids, and gases to lift a car?

STEM **Phenomenon** Auto mechanics often need to go under cars to repair the parts in the under-carriage, such as the shocks and exhaust

Student Discourse

California Elevate Science promotes active discussion, higher order thinking and analysis and prepares you for high school through:

- High-level write-in prompts
- Evidence-based arguments
- Practice in speaking and writing

Model It!

Crystalline and Amorphous Solids

Figure 5 A pat of butter is an amorphous solid. The particles that make up the butter are not arranged in a regular pattern. The sapphire gem stones are crystalline solids. Draw what you think the particles look like in a crystalline solid.

READING CHECK **Explain** In your own words, explain the main differences between crystalline solids and amorphous solids.

Quest CHECK-IN

In this lesson, you learned what happens to the particles of substances during melting, freezing, evaporation, boiling, condensation, and sublimation. You also thought about how thermal energy plays a role in these changes of state.

Predict Why do you need to take the temperature of the surroundings into consideration when designing a system with materials that can change state?

Academic Vocabulary

In orange juice, bits of pulp are suspended in liquid. Explain what you think *suspended* means.

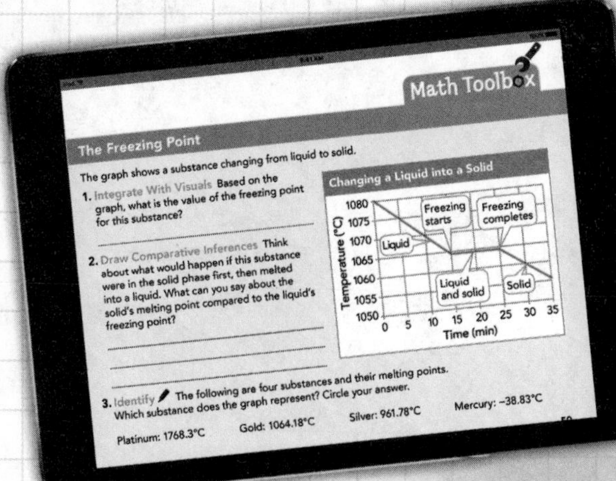

Build Literacy Skills

By connecting science to other disciplines like:

- Mathematics
- Reading and Writing
- STEM/Engineering

Focus on Inquiry

Case studies put you in the shoes of a scientist to solve real-world mysteries using real data. You will be able to:

- Analyze data
- Formulate claims
- Build evidence-based arguments

Case Study

MS-PS1-4

RISING to the OCCASION: Charles's Law in the Oven!

Have you ever baked bread or rolls? If so, you probably observed that during baking, the bread rises, increasing in volume. What causes this to happen? The answer lies in chemistry.

In the heat of an oven, gas bubbles in bread

Chemistry in Baking

Chemistry and baking go together naturally. In fact, chemistry affects every aspect of preparing food.

Enter the Digital Classroom

Virtual labs, 3-D expeditions, and dynamic videos take science beyond the classroom.

- Open-ended virtual labs
- Google Expeditions and field trips
- NBC Learn videos

Spotlight on the
Anchoring Phenomenon

How does an increased human population make it difficult to protect biodiversity?

Explore It

Look at the picture. What do you observe? What questions do you have about the phenomenon? Write your observations and questions in the space below.

California Spotlight

Instructional Segment 4

MS-LS2-4 MS-LS2-5, MS-ESS2-2, MS-ESS3-2, EP&CIb, EP&CIc, EP&CIIa, EP&CIIb, EP&CIIc, EP&CIIIc, EP&CIVc, EP&CVa

Inquiry

- What natural processes and human activities threaten biodiversity and ecosystem services?
- How can people help sustain biodiversity and ecosystem services in a changing world?

Topics

8 Plate Tectonics

9 Earth's Surface Systems

10 Populations, Communities, and Ecosystems

Before the Topics

Identify the Problem

California Floristic Province

Phenomenon California is one of the most biologically diverse places in the world! The state is home to an amazing number of different plant and animal species.

However, the needs of an increasing human population can make it difficult to protect California's biodiversity.

View of the California coastline from the Bixby Bridge in Big Sur

Biodiversity Hotspots

Scientists have identified several areas on Earth as being *biodiversity hotspots.* A biodiversity hotspot is an area that supports an especially high number of endemic species that do not exist anywhere else, and is also rapidly losing biodiversity. Hotspots are critical to global biodiversity. Only two biodiversity hotspots exist in North America; the California Floristic Province is one of them.

The California Floristic Province is characterized by hot, dry summers and cool, wet winters. It is considered to be a Mediterranean climate. The California Floristic Province is made up of many different habitats and ecosystems such as mountains, volcanoes, deserts, forests, salt marshes, and vernal pools. These diverse ecosystems are home to 3,488 species of plants, of which 2,124 are endemic, or native.

Look at the table to see the number of diverse and endemic species identified in the California Floristic Province.

The California Floristic Province begins in southwestern Oregon, covers a majority of California, and ends in northwest Baja California, Mexico.

SEP Use Mathematics Complete the table by calculating the percentage of each category of endemic species.

Types of Organism	Species	Endemic Species	Percent Endemic
Plants	3,488	2,124	
Mammals	157	18	
Birds	340	8	
Reptiles	69	4	
Amphibians	46	25	
Freshwater Fishes	73	15	

Physical Diversity of California

The landscape of California is due in large part to plate tectonics and other natural processes. As tectonic plates have moved, shifted, and collided with one another, landforms and geographic features have formed. Earthquake fault lines, volcanoes, and mountains are some examples. Over time, some of these landforms eroded and contributed to the soil. As a result, California is known to have the greatest diversity of soils in the U.S. This characteristic has allowed such diverse and endemic plant life to thrive in the California Floristic Province.

California's landscape is due to the movement of Earth's plates, which has resulted in volcanoes, mountains, and earthquakes.

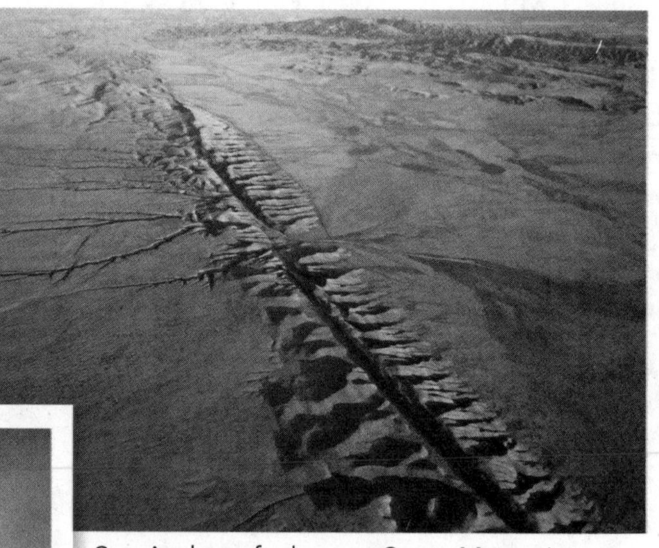

San Andreas fault, near Santa Margarita, California

Mt. Lassen, an active volcano in the northeastern part of the state, near Mineral, California

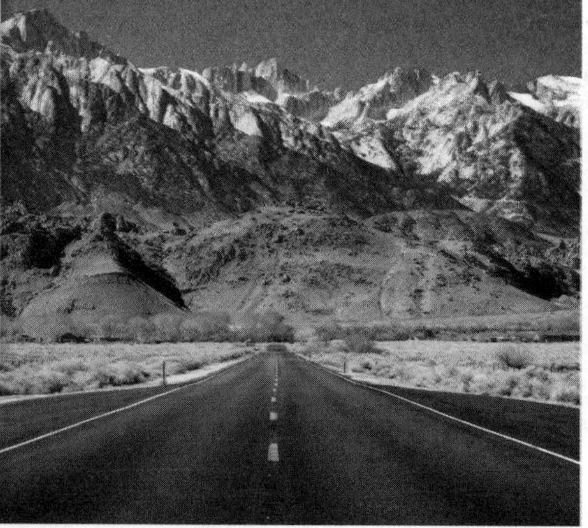

Mt. Whitney, the tallest mountain in the contiguous United States, near Lone Pine, California

Threats to the Province

As California's human population increases, so does the demand for basic needs such as housing, food, and energy. To meet the demands of a growing human population, habitats are often destroyed to make room for new homes, roads, agriculture, and the extraction of energy sources such as oil. When an ecosystem is negatively impacted, the benefits humans receive from ecosystems are also affected. These benefits are called ecosystem services. Changes to habitats and ecosystems can also cause different types of pollution and erosion.

Commercial agriculture and farming are not only important to the residents of California, but also to the rest of the country. The rich soils in the California Floristic Province allow for plant diversity, and they help to generate many of the agricultural products consumed in the U.S. Scientists estimate that 75% of the vegetation that was originally found in the California Floristic Province has been damaged or lost.

About 43 million acres of California's land are used for agriculture. Grazing land takes up 16 million acres, while there are 27 million acres of cropland.

SEP Construct Explanations How do natural processes and human activities impact biodiversity and ecosystem services in the California Floristic Province?

....

....

....

Protecting the Province

Throughout this segment, you will learn about plate tectonics, earthquakes, volcanoes, weathering and soil, erosion and deposition, ecosystems, ecosystem services, and biodiversity. Scientists need to understand the relationships between Earth's natural processes, ecosystems, and the role of humans in order to protect the California Floristic Province.

California is often thought to be a forerunner in establishing conservation efforts and environmental policies. For example, the California Biodiversity Council was established in 1991 to help improve cooperation between environmental preservation and conservation groups at the federal, state, and local levels. Members of the council exchange ideas, solve problems, and discuss and develop strategies to conserve California's biodiversity. While steps have been taken to preserve the biodiversity of the California Floristic Province hotspot, more still needs to be done. Currently, only 37 percent of the total land area of the California Floristic Province is officially protected.

Establishing national parks and breeding programs are just some examples of how biodiversity has been protected in California.

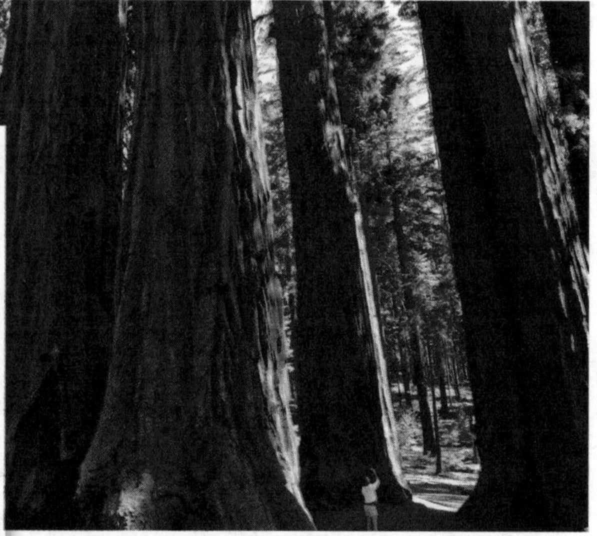

The largest trees in the world grow in the protected lands of Sequoia National Park, near Visalia, California.

The California condor, the largest bird in North America, is found within the California Floristic Province.

Ask Questions

What questions can you ask to help you make sense of this phenomena?

TOPIC

8

Plate Tectonics

Investigative Phenomenon

Why is it important to analyze and interpret data to provide evidence for past plate motions?

MS-ESS2-2 Construct an explanation based on evidence for how geoscience processes have changed Earth's surface at varying time and spatial scales.

MS-ESS2-3 Analyze and interpret data on the distribution of fossils and rocks, continental shapes, and seafloor structures to provide evidence of the past plate motions.

MS-ESS3-2 Analyze and interpret data on natural hazards to forecast future catastrophic events and inform the development of technologies to mitigate their effects.

EP&CIb Students should be developing an understanding that the ecosystem services provided by natural systems are essential to human life and to the functioning of our economies and cultures.

HANDS-ON LAB

uConnect Explore how Earth's continents can be linked together.

How did these chain islands get here?

What questions do you have about the phenomenon?

Quest PBL

To Hike or Not to Hike

STEM **Figure It Out** Camping and hiking in the mountains are popular pastimes for people all over the world. But are you safe if the mountain is actually an active volcano? It hasn't erupted for thousands of years—but it *could.* Would volcanologists say it is safe to hike? What kinds of data do they collect to predict eruptions? In this problem-based Quest activity, you will determine whether it is safe to take an extended camping and hiking trip on Mount Rainier. Through hands-on labs and digital activities, you'll gather evidence about Rainier's history and look into current research on the mountain's volcanic activity. You will use this information to create a presentation that supports your claim and synthesizes your findings.

INTERACTIVITY

To Hike or Not to Hike

MS-ESS2-2, MS-ESS3-2

After watching the Quest Kickoff video, which explains volcanic processes, think about the pros and cons of hiking on Mount Rainier. Record your ideas.

PROS

....

....

....

CONS

....

....

....

Quest CHECK-IN

IN LESSON 1

STEM What is Mount Rainier's history of eruption? Investigate the history of the Cascade Range and draw conclusions about the likelihood of an eruption.

HANDS-ON LAB

Patterns in the Cascade Range

Quest CHECK-IN

IN LESSON 2

How is volcanic activity related to tectonic plate movements? Explore the science behind the connection.

INTERACTIVITY

Mount Rainier's Threat

Quest CHECK-IN

IN LESSON 3

What processes cause earthquakes and tsunamis to form? Think about the possible risks from movements of the ground beneath your feet.

INTERACTIVITY

Monitoring a Volcano

The Cascade Range stretches from northern California northward through British Columbia, Canada. Mount Rainier is just one of many volcanoes that lie within the range and are considered "active."

Quest CHECK-IN

STEM IN LESSON 4

What kinds of data can be used to predict an eruption? Investigate the tools and methods that volcanologists use to study volcanoes. Then analyze some data to determine the likelihood of an eruption.

HANDS-ON LAB

Signs of Eruption?

Quest FINDINGS

Complete the Quest!

Present information on Mount Rainier's history and current geological research, along with your evidence-based argument about whether it is safe to hike and camp there.

INTERACTIVITY

Reflect on Mount Rainier's Safety

LESSON 1

Evidence of Plate Motions

HANDS-ON LAB

uInvestigate Piece Pangaea together.

MS-ESS2-3 Analyze and interpret data on the distribution of fossils and rocks, continental shapes, and seafloor structures to provide evidence of the past plate motions.

Connect It!

Draw lines between South America and Africa to show how the contours of the two continents could fit together.

CCC Stability and Change What might you infer about South America and Africa if you thought the continents were movable objects?

Hypothesis of Continental Drift

For many centuries, scientists and map-makers had been curious about why some continents look as though they could fit together like the pieces of a jigsaw puzzle. The continents on the east and west sides of the South Atlantic Ocean, for example, looked like they would fit together perfectly (**Figure 1**). In the mid 1800s, scientists began to gather clues that suggested the slow movement, or drift, of continents. In 1912, German meteorologist Alfred Wegener (VAY guh nur) further developed the **hypothesis** that all of of the continents had once been joined together, and that over time they had moved great distances and spread apart. This hypothesis became known as "continental drift."

In 1915, after gathering evidence that supported the hypothesis, Wegener published *The Origin of Continents and Oceans*. The book connected clues from investigations of land features, types of rock, fossils (traces of organisms preserved in rock), and climate. Evidence at local and global scales led Wegener to map ancient land and water patterns. He made a compelling case for the hypothesis that a supercontinent called Pangaea (pan JEE uh) had broken up into the continents we know today.

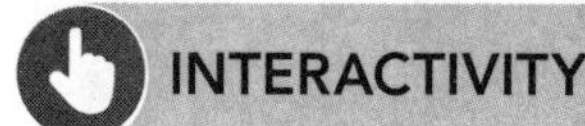

Try your hand at piecing together puzzles.

Academic Vocabulary

In science, a hypothesis is an idea that can be tested through experimentation or investigation. It is an evidence-based idea that serves as a starting point, whereas a scientific theory is what science produces when a hypothesis has been shown to be true through a broad range of studies. As you read this lesson, highlight or underline the key components of the hypothesis of continental drift.

Pieces of the Puzzle

Figure 1 Scientists wondered whether the continents' coastlines seemed to fit like jigsaw puzzle pieces because they had once been joined together. The light blue areas east of South America and west of Africa are continental shelves. Those areas are parts of the continents, but they are covered by shallow seawater.

Literacy Connection

Cite Textual Evidence Use your science notebook to organize the evidence that supports the hypothesis of continental drift. Identify a common theme among the different pieces of evidence.

Evidence From Land Features There were other pieces of evidence to support the hypothesis of continental drift. Mountain ranges near those continents' coasts seemed to line up, as though they had been made in the same place and at the same time. Coal deposits, made of the remains of plants that thrived in warm locations millions of years ago, were found on multiple continents and in regions that no longer supported that kind of plant life. The similarity of features found in separate, scattered locations (**Figure 2**) suggested that they hadn't always been separate.

Evidence From Fossils Geologists noticed that evidence from the fossil record supported continental drift. (**Figure 2**). Geologist Edward Suess noted that fossils of *Glossopteris* (glaw SAHP tuh ris), a fernlike plant from 250 million years ago, were found on five continents. This suggested that those landmasses had once been connected, as part of Pangaea. Fossils of animals told a similar story. *Mesosaurus* was a reptile that lived in fresh-water habitats millions of years ago, yet *Mesosaurus* fossils were found in the same types of rock in both South America and Africa.

Evidence for Continental Drift

Figure 2 Study the map key to see how Wegener pieced together similar pieces of evidence from separate sites to support his hypothesis. Then integrate technical information from the text with the version of the information shown in the diagram.

Integrate with Visuals Present-day India is in South Asia, at the northern end of the Indian Ocean. What evidence found in India matches that of other locations?

....

....

....

PACIFIC OCEAN

Evidence From Climate Wegener, whose own expertise was in the study of weather and climate and not geology, also gathered evidence that showed Earth's continents had experienced different climates than the ones they have today. For example, Spitsbergen, an island in the Arctic Ocean, has fossils of plants that could have survived only in a tropical climate. This doesn't mean that the Arctic Ocean once had a tropical climate. That isn't possible, because the poles do not receive enough sunlight to produce tropical weather or support tropical plants. Instead, this evidence means Spitsbergen used to be near the equator, part of a supercontinent. The supercontinent slowly broke apart, and the island now known as Spitsbergen drifted far to the north over the course of millions of years. Interactions at time scales from the lifetime of a plant to millions of years can be understood in terms of moving continents.

CHECK POINT **Summarize Text** What is the general pattern in the evidence that supports the hypothesis of continental drift?

....

....

HANDS-ON LAB

Investigate Piece Pangaea together.

Reflect Think of some organic item (such as a flower or type of fruit) that you've found in at least two places that are many miles apart. Do the items have a common origin? Why do you think so? What conclusions can you draw from the item's presence in widely different locations?

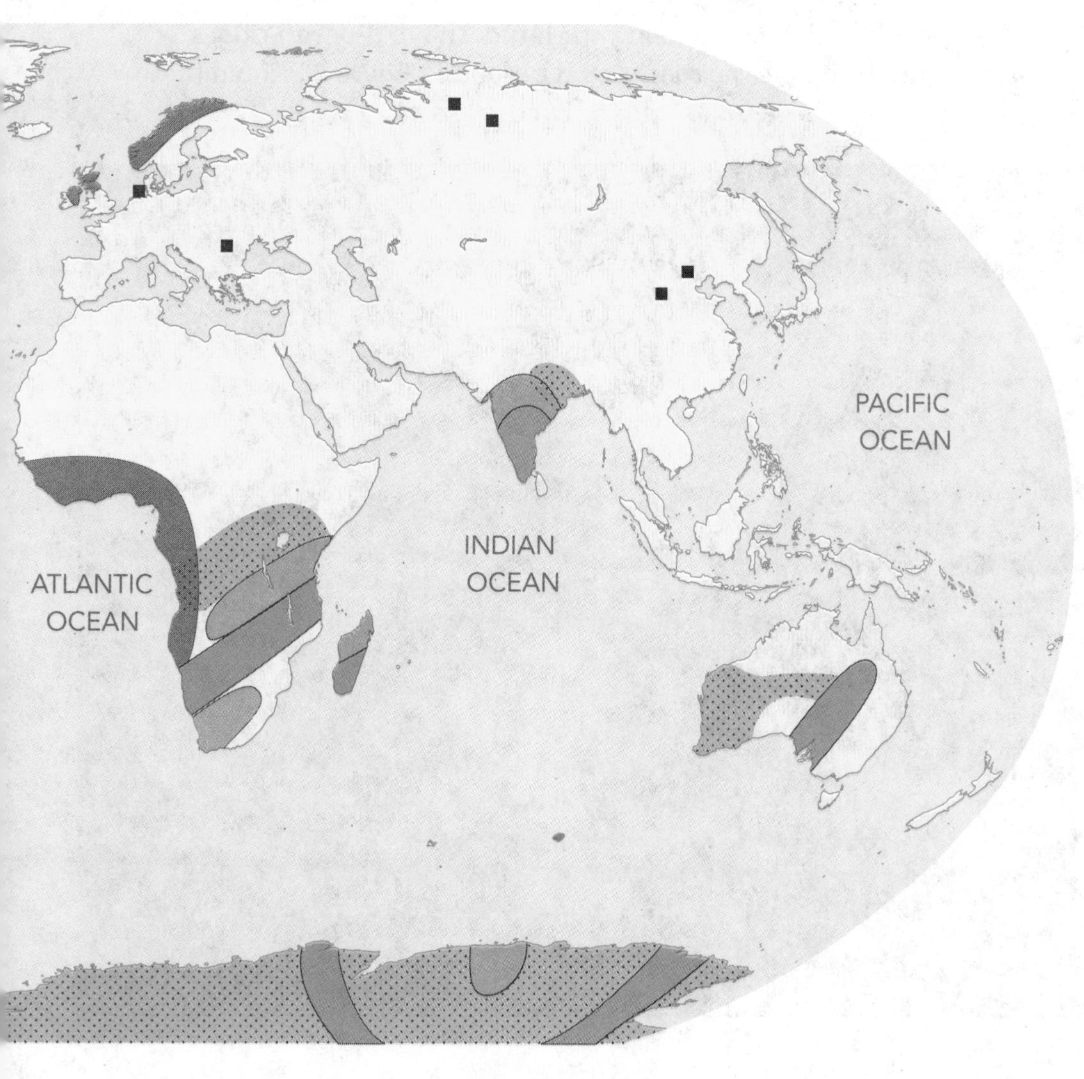

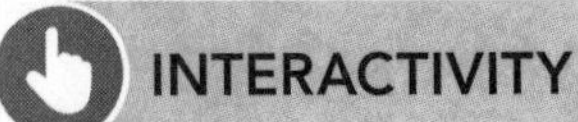

INTERACTIVITY

Investigate patterns on land and on the seafloor.

Mid-Ocean Ridges

The hypothesis of continental drift included evidence from different areas of science, but it had a major flaw. It lacked a good explanation for *how* the continents could have broken up and moved apart. Many scientists rejected the hypothesis for that reason. By the middle of the 1900s, advances in oceanography—the study of Earth's oceans—allowed a mapping of the ocean floor that renewed interest in continental drift. Undersea exploration provided evidence that Earth's surface was composed of moving plates—large pieces of the lithosphere.

By measuring distances from the sea surface to its floor, scientists now had a clear picture of what Earth's surface looked like under the oceans. What surprised many was the presence of long, zipper-like chains of undersea mountains called **mid-ocean ridges**. One such chain, called the Mid-Atlantic Ridge, ran down the middle of the Atlantic Ocean, curving in a pattern that seemed to mirror the contours of the surrounding continental coastlines. Further modeling and mapping of the ocean floor in the 1990s showed that these mid-ocean ridges extend throughout Earth's oceans for about 70,000 kilometers. If you could hold Earth in your hand, the mid-ocean ridges might resemble the seams on a baseball (**Figure 3**). Could these ridges be the actual seams of Earth's crust?

Mid-Ocean Ridges

Figure 3 Mapping of mid-ocean ridges in the mid-1900s provided supporting evidence that Earth's surface was composed of moving plates.

Integrate with Visuals Do any of the mid-ocean ridges appear to extend into continents? Explain which ones.

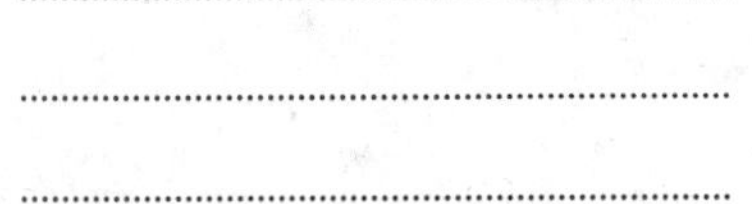

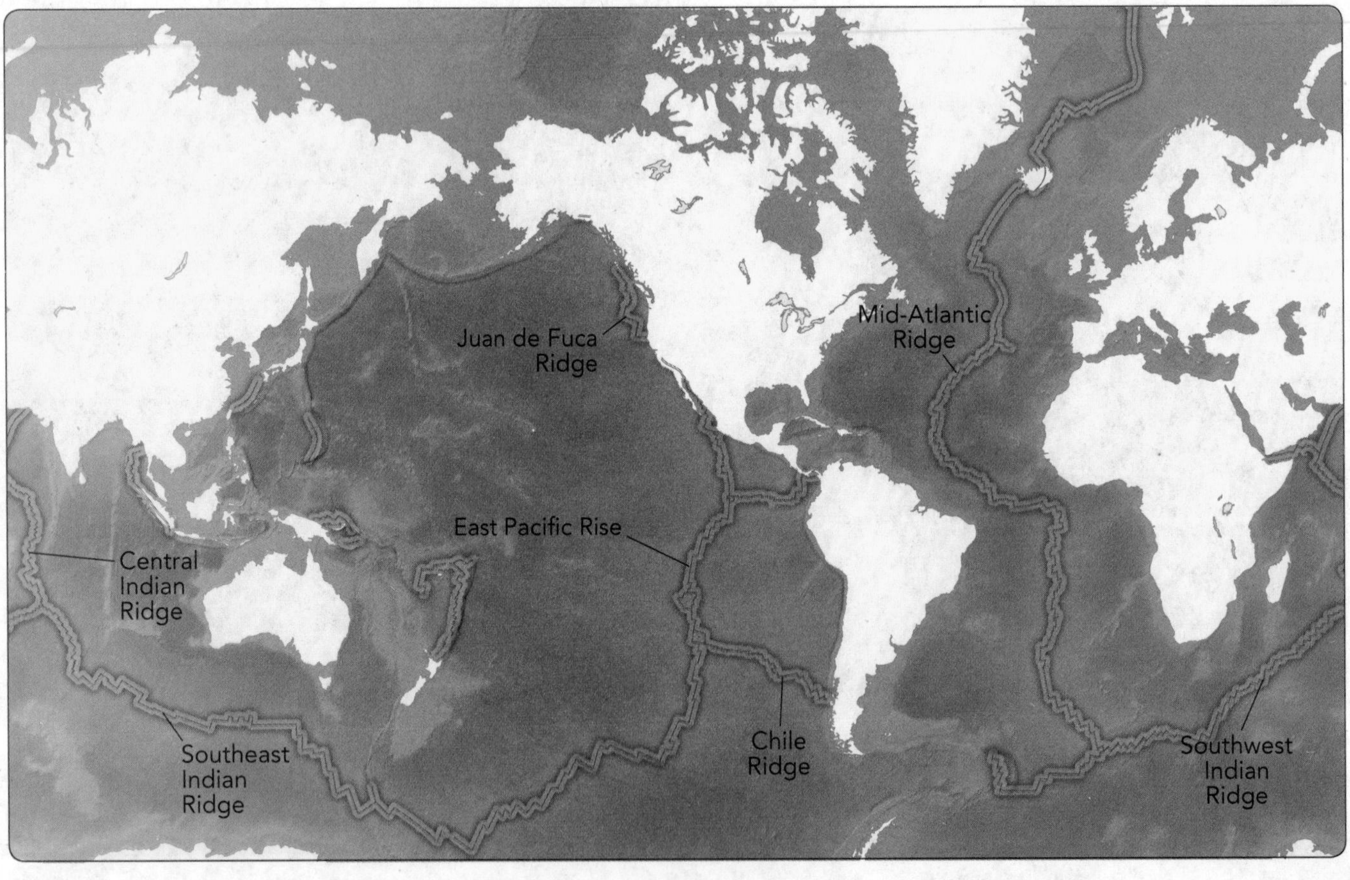

Juan de Fuca Ridge
Mid-Atlantic Ridge
East Pacific Rise
Central Indian Ridge
Southeast Indian Ridge
Chile Ridge
Southwest Indian Ridge

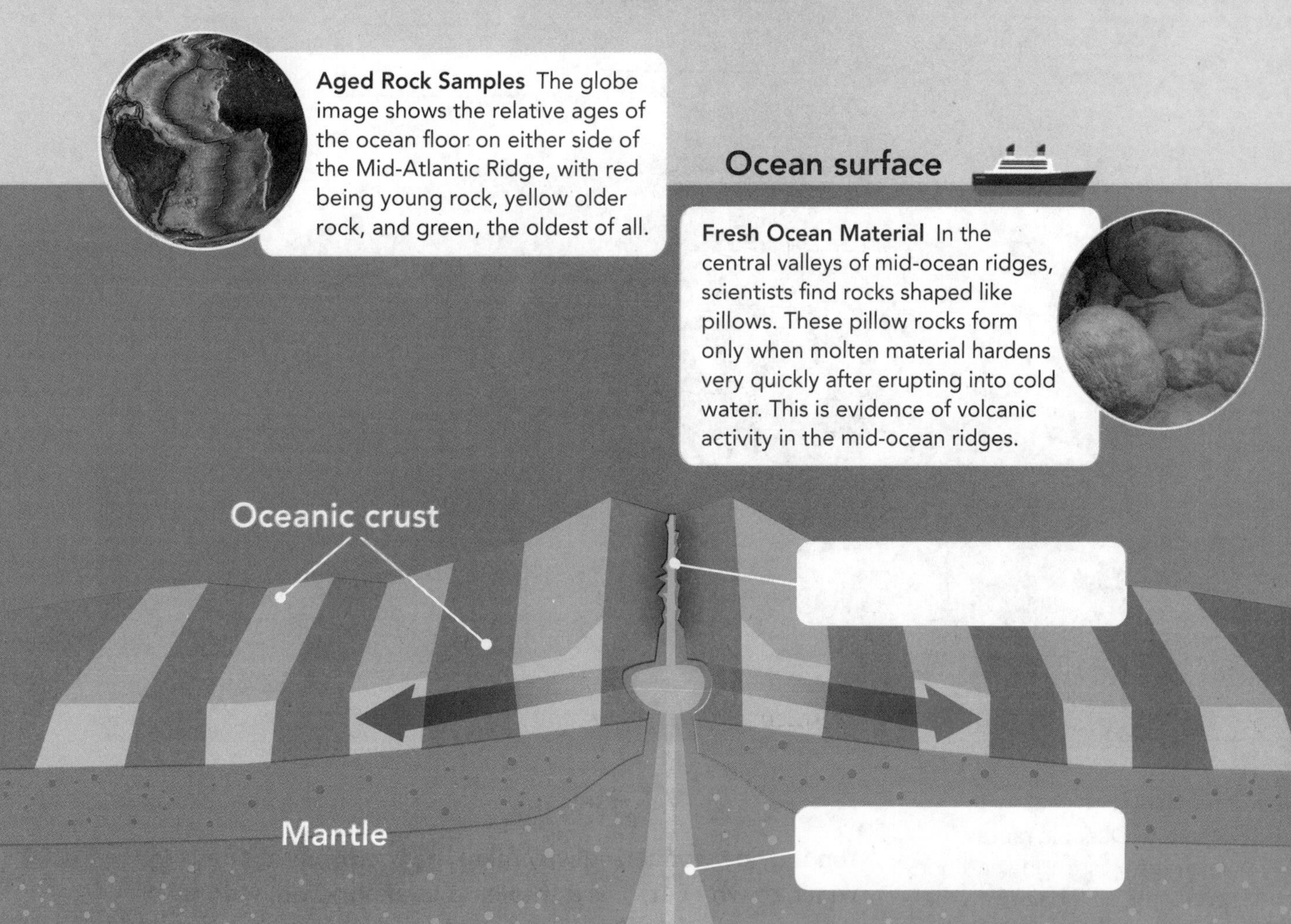
Aged Rock Samples The globe image shows the relative ages of the ocean floor on either side of the Mid-Atlantic Ridge, with red being young rock, yellow older rock, and green, the oldest of all.
Ocean surface
Fresh Ocean Material In the central valleys of mid-ocean ridges, scientists find rocks shaped like pillows. These pillow rocks form only when molten material hardens very quickly after erupting into cold water. This is evidence of volcanic activity in the mid-ocean ridges.
Oceanic crust
Mantle

Sea-Floor Spreading

While ocean-floor mapping was underway, geologists began to gather samples of rock from the ocean floor. They learned that mid-ocean ridges are the sources of new spans of the ocean floor. In a process called **sea-floor spreading**, molten rock flows up through a crack in Earth's crust and hardens into solid strips of new rock on both sides of the crack. The entire floor on either side of the ridge moves away when this occurs, meaning the older strips of rock move farther from the ridge over time. It's like a pair of conveyer belts, with new material appearing at the ridge while older material is carried away. The process goes on at a scale too large to see, so scientists use models. **Figure 4** shows such a model and describes some specific evidence of sea-floor spreading.

Sea-Floor Spreading

Figure 4 Sea-floor spreading continually adds material to the ocean floor on both sides of the ridge.

SEP Develop Models Label the different features that play a role in sea-floor spreading.

CHECK POINT **Cite Textual Evidence** Why was undersea exploration important for developing the theory of plate tectonics?

....

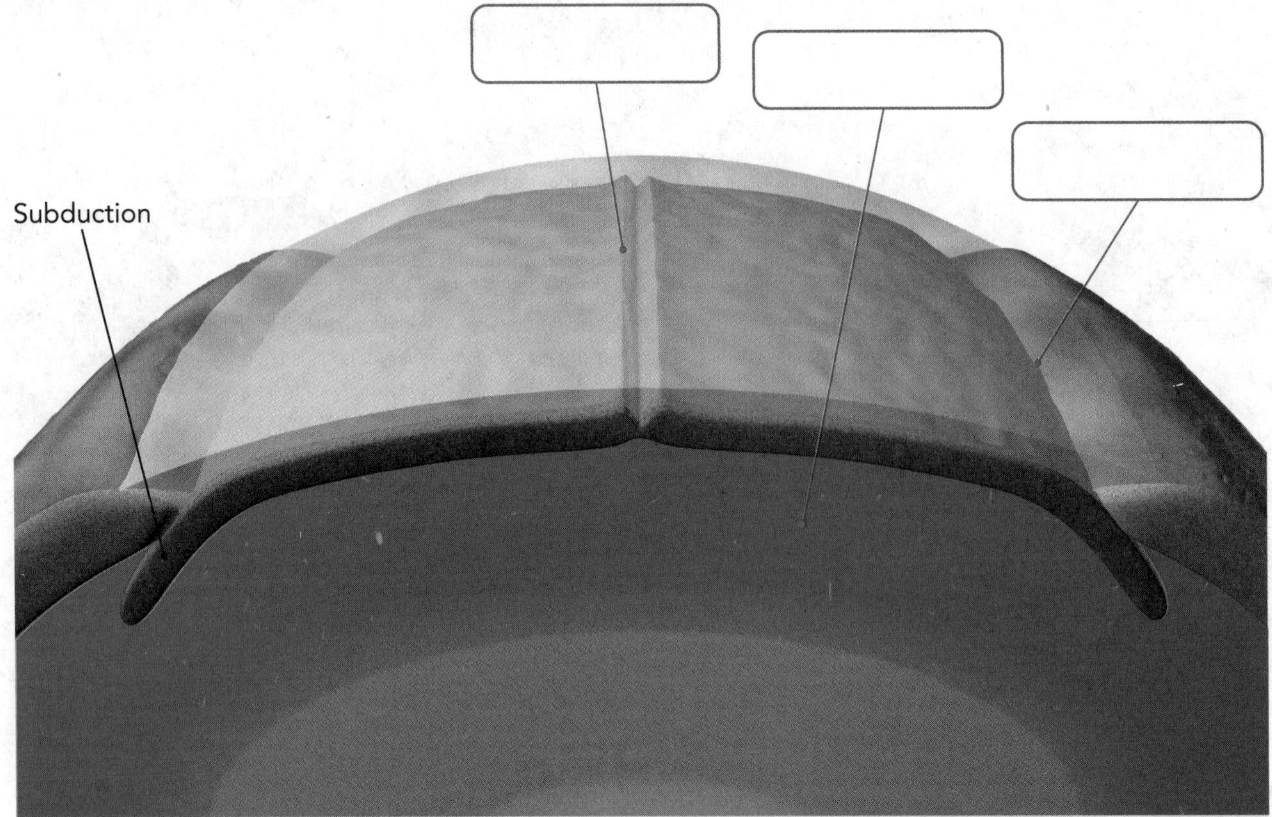

Subduction

Figure 5 Oceanic plates, which form through sea-floor spreading, sink back into the mantle at subduction zones.

CCC System Models

Label the mantle, mid-ocean ridge, and ocean trench.

Ocean Trenches

You may be wondering why all of the oceans aren't getting wider, or why Earth as a whole is not expanding, with all of the sea-floor spreading going on. The answer to that is **subduction** (sub DUC shun), or the sinking movement of ocean floor back into the mantle. Subduction occurs where a dense plate of oceanic crust goes under an adjacent section of Earth's crust. This occurs at **ocean trenches**, which are undersea valleys that are the deepest parts of the ocean (**Figure 5**).

The Process of Subduction New oceanic crust is relatively warm. As the rock cools and moves away from a mid-ocean ridge, it gets denser. At some point, the dense slab of oceanic crust may meet another section of ocean floor, or a continent. What happens? Because the oceanic crust is cooler than the mantle underneath, it is denser and will sink into the mantle if given the chance. At an ocean trench, it has that chance, and the oceanic crust will sink under the edge of a continent or a younger, less-dense slab of oceanic crust. The oceanic plate that sinks back into the mantle gets recycled. This process can produce volcanic eruptions at the surface. If the oceanic crust meets continental crust, then a chain of volcanoes will form. If it meets more oceanic crust, then there will likely be a chain of volcanic islands.

VIDEO

Watch what happens at ocean ridges and trenches.

Subduction and the Oceans An ocean basin can have a spreading ridge, subduction zones, or both, depending on its age. The Atlantic Ocean, for example, has the Mid-Atlantic Ridge running down its full length, but no subduction zones. This means that the Atlantic Ocean is still getting wider—by about 2 to 5 centimeters per year. At some point, part of the oceanic plate will begin to sink back into the mantle and a subduction zone will form.

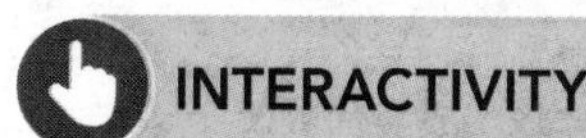

Learn about the slow and steady movement on Earth.

The Pacific Ocean is a more mature ocean basin. While it still has a spreading ridge, the Pacific basin is surrounded by subduction zones. The oceanic crust in the Pacific is being recycled back into the mantle faster than it is being created. This means that the Pacific Ocean basin is getting smaller.

The interactions that have shaped Earth's history will determine its future. Eventually, hundreds of millions of years from now, as Africa collides with Europe, and the Pacific Ocean closes up, a new supercontinent may appear.

CHECK POINT **Cite Textual Evidence** What features are evidence of the Pacific Ocean's maturity?

....

Model It!

Predict North America's Movement

Figure 6 The map shows the layout of some of Earth's landmasses, the mid-ocean ridges where plates are made, and ocean trenches where plates are recycled.

CCC Stability and Change Draw a line to indicate where you think the west coast of North America will eventually be located.

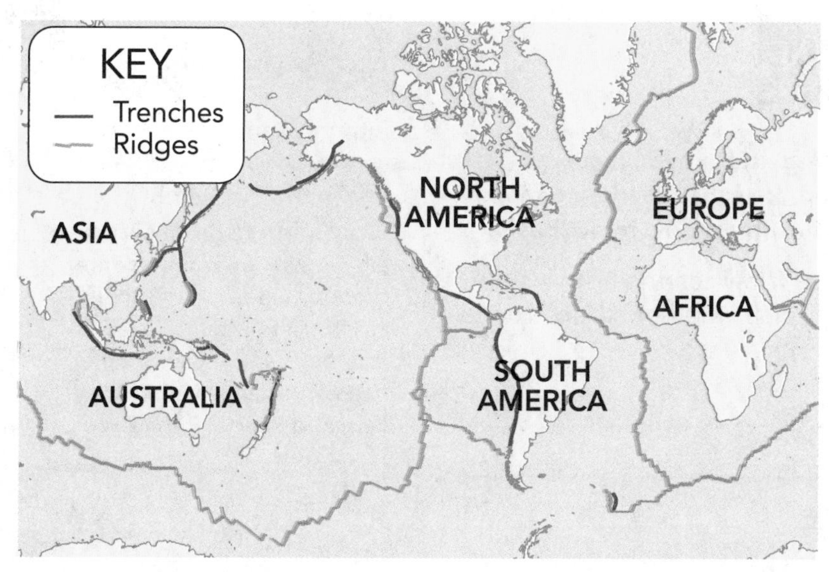

LESSON 1 Check

MS-ESS2-3

1. **SEP Communicate Information** Describe the hypothesis of continental drift.

   The hypothesis for the continental drift is that the continents used to be together but then drifted apart.

2. **SEP Analyze Data** How did the study of fossils provide support for the ideas behind the existence of Pangaea?

   The study supports continental Animals and plants can't grow properly because of fossils.

3. **SEP Interpret Data** How did the discovery of mid-ocean ridges support the hypothesis of continental drift?

   The ocean trenches push the continents away.

4. **CCC Cause and Effect** A large oceanic crust collides with the edge of a continent. What will happen?

   the continents would then join together or destroy each other.

5. **Infer** A remotely-operated vehicle is sent to the deepest part of the Mariana Trench. It returns with a sample of rock from the ocean floor. Would this rock be old or young? Explain.

   I think this rock would be young becaus the older rocks are pushed away.

Quest CHECK-IN

In this lesson you learned about Wegener's hypothesis of continental drift and how he pieced together evidence from different areas of natural history to support his hypothesis.

Connect to the Nature of Science How can the history of Mount Rainier's eruptions help you decide whether hiking around Mount Rainier is safe?

HANDS-ON LAB

Patterns in the Cascade Range

Go online to download the lab worksheet. Analyze data to determine whether there is a pattern to Mount Rainier's eruptions and those of other nearby volcanoes in the Cascade Range of the Pacific Northwest.

IT'S ALL CONNECTED SCIENCE SOCIAL STUDIES

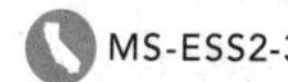

The Slow Acceptance of Continental Drift

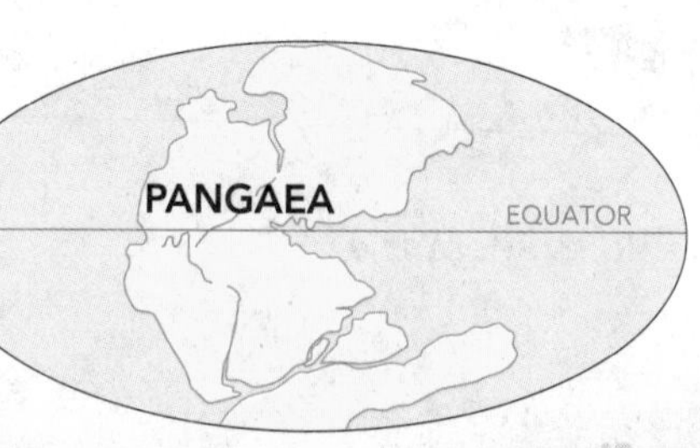

"Utter rot," a "fairy tale," and "delirious ravings." These statements are how some scientists in the early 1900s responded to Alfred Wegener's book describing the hypothesis of continental drift.

This case demonstrates that scientific thought doesn't always advance neatly or without controversy. Long-held scientific attitudes can be slow to change when new evidence or interpretations are encountered.

The hypothesis of continental drift faced a number of challenges. Though there was evidence to support it, there was not a convincing explanation of how continental drift actually occurred. Scientists who were skeptical of the idea heaped ridicule on Wegener.

In addition, Wegener was a trained meteorologist, but the hypothesis crossed multiple scientific disciplines. Many experts in their respective fields felt threatened because Wegener—viewed as an outsider—challenged their authority and expertise. After his death in 1930, continental drift was virtually ignored.

By the early 1960s, geologists had overcome many of the technological limitations of Wegener's time. They understood more about geological forces, and they were able to explain the mechanism by which the continents moved. The ideas behind continental drift reemerged as the theory of plate tectonics.

CONNECT TO YOU

Do you think skepticism is an important quality for a scientist to have? Explain why or why not. Discuss your ideas with a partner.

Wegener often took research trips to Greenland to study its climate. By taking core samples of ice, climatologists can learn about the climate of the past.

LESSON 2

Plate Tectonics and Earth's Surface

HANDS-ON LAB

uInvestigate Explore different plate interactions.

MS-ESS2-2 Construct an explanation based on evidence for how geoscience processes have changed Earth's surface at varying time and spatial scales.

Connect It!

Identify where the Himalaya Mountains are and circle them.

CCC Stability and Change Scientists are measuring Mount Everest to determine whether its height has changed. Why would the Himalayas be getting taller?

....

....

....

The Theory of Plate Tectonics

Investigate the role of stress in changing Earth's surface.

With observations of many geologists in the 1950s and 1960s, particularly of the features of the ocean floor, the ideas behind continental drift re-emerged as the **theory** of plate tectonics. This theory states that Earth's lithosphere—the crust and upper part of the mantle—is broken up into distinct plates. The plates are puzzle-like pieces that are in slow, constant motion relative to each other due to forces within the mantle. The theory explains the specific patterns of motion among the plates, including the different types of boundaries where they meet and the events and features that occur at their boundaries (**Figure 1**). The term *tectonic* refers to Earth's crust and to the large-scale processes that occur within it.

Academic Vocabulary

In science, the term *theory* is applied only to ideas that are supported by a vast, diverse array of evidence. How is the term used in everyday life?

....

....

....

....

....

....

Plate Tectonics Give Rise to the Himalayas

Figure 1 The tallest mountains on Earth, K2 and Mount Everest, are part of the Himalayas. When the landmass that is now known as India collided with Asia, these mountains began to form.

Convection Currents

Figure 2 In a pot of boiling water, warmer water rises and cooler water sinks to take its place. This movement creates convection currents in the pot of water.

Convection Drives Plate Motions The tectonic plates move because they are part of convection currents in the mantle. You may recall that convection is a cyclical movement of fluid driven by temperature differences at the top and bottom, such as cold water sinking from the surface and warm water rising from below (**Figure 2**). Convection occurs in the mantle where rock flows in slow-moving currents. These currents are responsible for moving the continents great distances across Earth's surface, even if they move at speeds too slow to be noticed.

Types of Crust Plates consist of one or two types of crust. Oceanic crust is the dense type of crust that is found at the bottom of the ocean (**Figure 3**). Some plates, such as the Pacific Plate, consist entirely of oceanic crust. The other type of crust is called continental crust. It is less dense than oceanic crust and is almost always thicker. As a result, the surfaces of continents are above sea level.

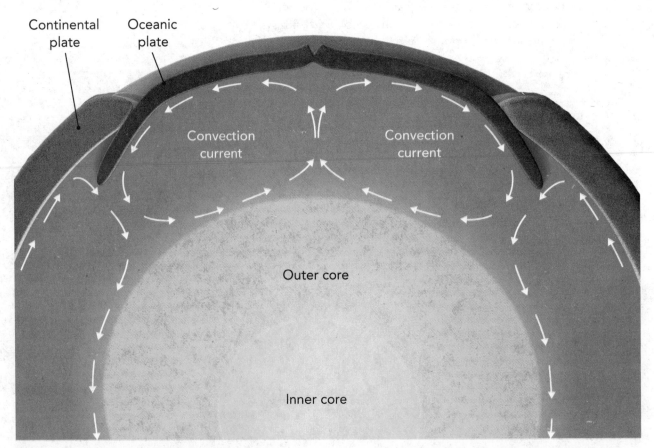

Oceanic and Continental Crust

Figure 3 The very dense crust of the ocean floor is oceanic crust. Crust that is less dense can be thick enough that it's above sea level, which is the case for the continents. The crust that makes up the continents is called continental crust.

Integrate with Visuals Use the directions in which the convection currents are moving in the figure to draw in arrows indicating the direction of the oceanic plates.

Pangaea

Equator

200 Million Years Ago

115 Million Years Ago

Equator

North America

Europe

Asia

Africa

Equator

South America

Australia

Antarctica

Earth Today

Plate Motions Over Time Scientists use satellites to measure plate motions precisely. The plates move very slowly—about 1 to 10 centimeters per year. The plates that carry North America and Eurasia, move apart at a rate of 1 to 2 centimeters per year, or about as fast as your fingernails grow. The process is slow on a daily scale, but on a scale of billions of years, the plates have moved great distances.

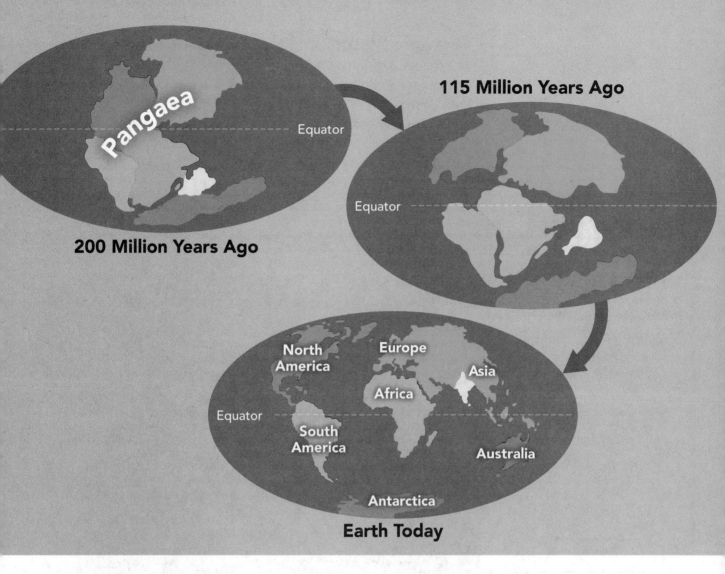

Over time, the movement of Earth's plates has greatly changed the locations of the continents and the size and shape of the ocean basins. Long before Pangaea existed, over billions of years, other supercontinents had formed and split apart. Pangaea itself formed when Earth's plates collided about 350 to 250 million years ago. Then, about 200 million years ago, Pangaea broke up and began to spread apart (**Figure 4**).

CHECK POINT **Draw Conclusions** Suppose the interactions from Earth's history continue into the future. When might the continents of today form a new supercontinent?

....

200 Million Years of Plate Motions

Figure 4 Since the breakup of Pangaea, it has taken the continents about 200 million years to move to their present locations.

Integrate with Visuals Label the landmasses from 115 million years ago with the present-day names of continents, as shown on the "Earth Today" map.

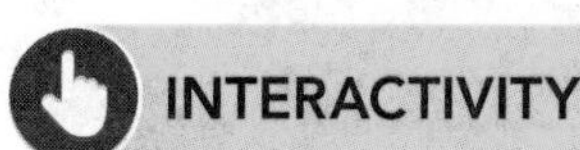

Compare the relative rates of motion of different plates.

Tectonic Plates and the "Ring of Fire"

The theory of plate tectonics predicts that earthquakes and volcanoes should occur at plate boundaries, and that some landforms, such as mountain ranges, should mark the plate boundaries. For example, many volcanic eruptions and earthquakes occur at the edges of the Pacific Plate (**Figure 5**), which lies under the Pacific Ocean.

Model It!

Ring of Fire

Figure 5 Because the region around the Pacific Ocean is prone to volcanic activity and earthquakes, it is known as the "Ring of Fire."

1. **Claim** Why do so many volcanoes seem to occur on coastlines of the Pacific Ocean?

....

....

....

....

....

....

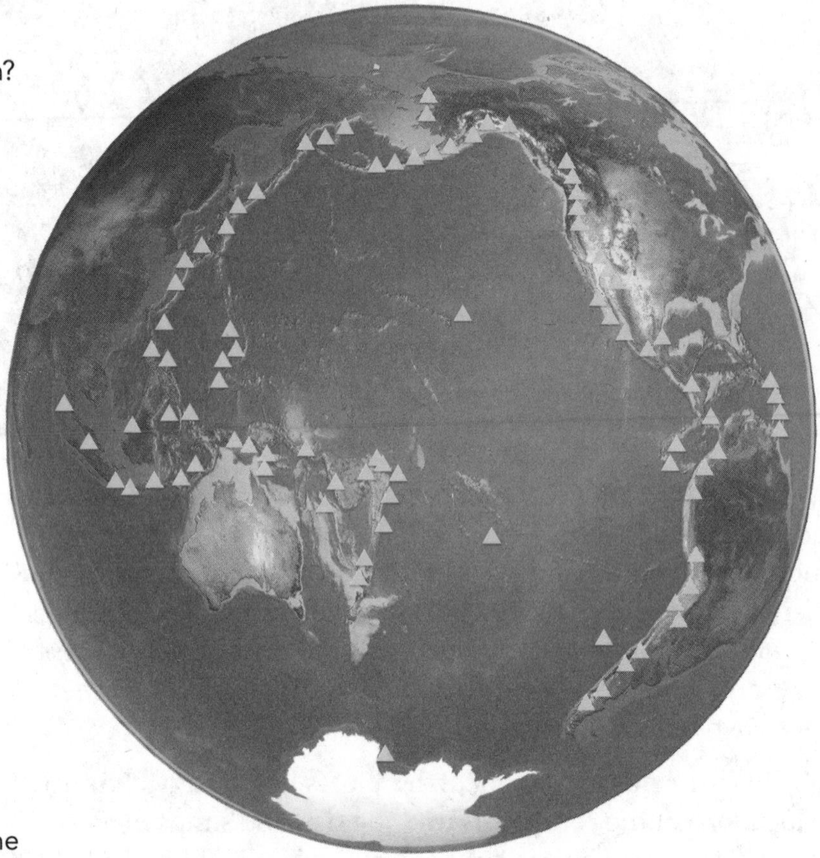

▲ Volcanoes

2. **Evidence** According to the theory of plate tectonics, how do the locations of volcanoes compare with plate boundaries? On **Figure 5,** draw the edges of the different plates, including the Pacific Plate. Use **Figure 6** to help you.

3. **Reasoning** Describe how the symbols on the map guided your markup of the map.

....

....

Plate Map

Figure 6 Scientists have identified the different tectonic plates, many of which are named for the continents they carry. The boundaries are either convergent, divergent, or transform. Relative plate movements at some of the boundaries are indicated with red arrows.

SEP Develop Models ✎ Using the map key as a reference, add the arrows that are missing in the circles provided.

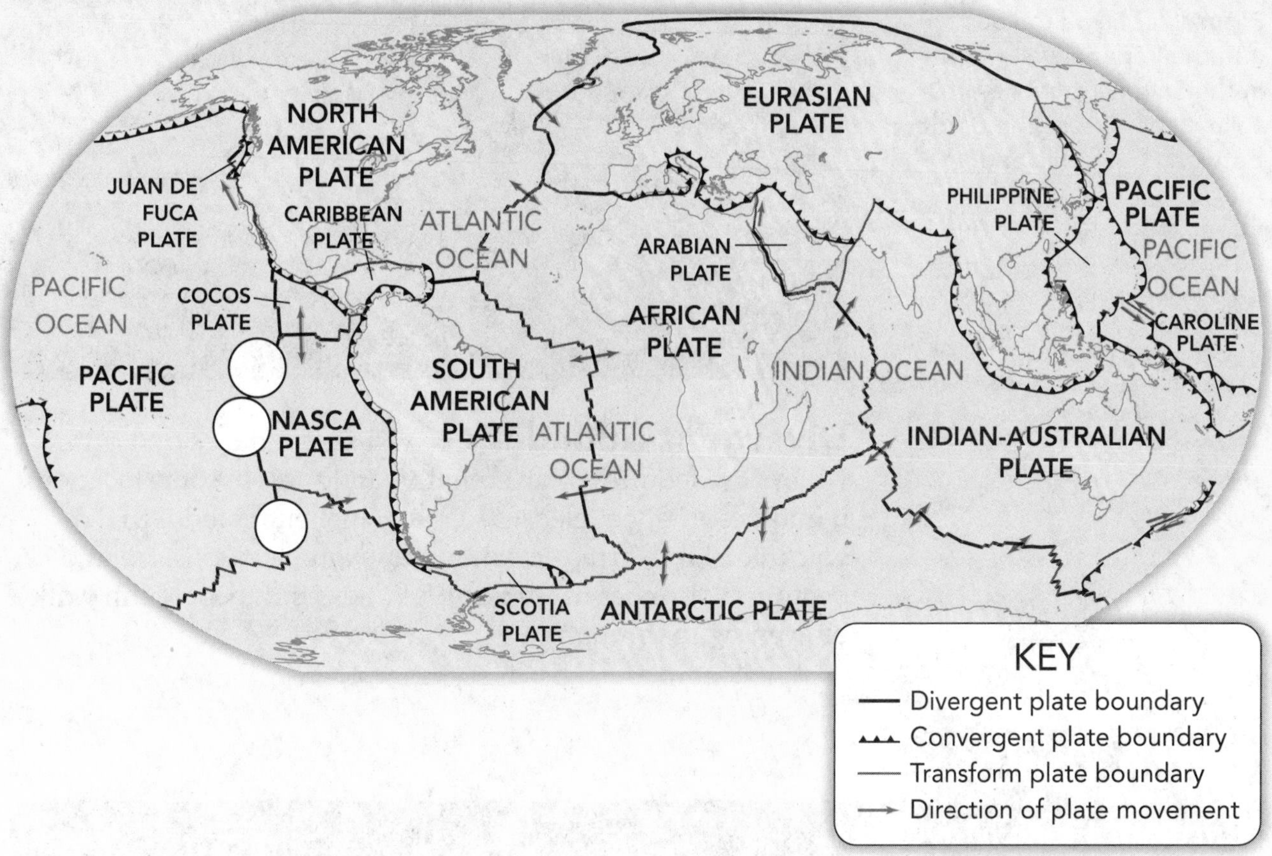

KEY
- Divergent plate boundary
- Convergent plate boundary
- Transform plate boundary
- Direction of plate movement

Plate Boundaries

Earth's plates meet and interact at boundaries. Along each boundary, plates move in one of three ways. Plates move apart, or diverge, from each other at a **divergent boundary** (dy VUR junt). Plates come together, or converge, at a **convergent boundary** (kun VER junt). Plates slip past each other along a **transform boundary**. The interactions of plates at boundaries produce great changes on land and on the ocean floor. These changes include the formation of volcanoes, mountain ranges, and deep-ocean trenches. Earthquakes and the triggering of tsunamis are also more common at or near plate boundaries. **Figure 6** depicts the major tectonic plates and the types of boundaries between them.

☑ CHECK POINT **Integrate with Visuals** Which of the plates from the map would be a good starting point for a diagram that summarizes the different boundaries? Explain.

....

....

Literacy Connection

Integrate with Visuals
In your science notebook, draw sketches of the different interactions at plate boundaries. Work toward a visual presentation that summarizes the plate boundaries in a single diagram.

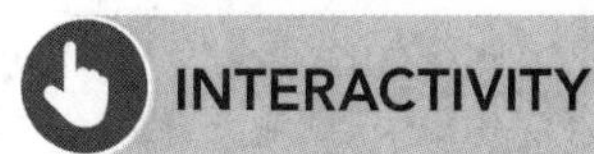

INTERACTIVITY

Explore surface features associated with plate movement at different locations around the world.

VIDEO

Learn about the tectonic plate boundary types.

Salton Trough

Figure 7 The Salton Sea and the Imperial Valley are in the Salton Trough, a rift valley that crosses the border between California and Mexico.

Divergent Boundaries Mid-ocean ridges and rift valleys are features of divergent boundaries. In some locations, a mid-ocean ridge releases so much molten material that a volcanic island forms. Iceland is an example of this. Iceland contains volcanoes as well as rift valleys that people can walk or even swim through.

Math Toolbox

Rates of Plate Movement

Earth scientists measure plate movement by using the Global Positioning System (GPS) of satellites. Receivers anchored in Earth's surface receive signals from satellites and calculate their positions using the time it takes for signals to be received. Patterns in the rate of change in those signals show the operation of the natural system of plate movement.

1. **Reason Quantitatively** GPS readings suggest that the Mid-Atlantic Ridge spreads about 2.5 cm per year. How fast is the North American Plate moving away from the ridge? Explain your answer.

2. **SEP Use Mathematics** The Pacific Plate moves to the northwest at an average rate of 10 cm per year. Hawaii is in the middle of the Pacific Plate, 6,600 kilometers southeast of Japan, which is on the edge of several adjacent plates. If the Pacific Plate continues to move at the same rate and in the same direction, when will Hawaii collide with Japan? Using the variable *t* for time, write and solve an equation.

Convergent Boundaries

A boundary where two plates collide, or move toward each other, is called a convergent boundary. If two continents collide, then a mountain range is pushed up, or uplifted. This is how the Himalayas formed, and they are still being uplifted. What is now India used to be a separate continent that broke away from Antarctica and headed north. It began colliding with Asia more than 60 million years ago, and the edges of the two plates folded like the hoods of two cars in a head-on collision (**Figure 8**). Mount Everest and the rest of the Himalayas are the result.

If one or both plates are oceanic, then subduction occurs. The ocean plate always subducts if it collides with a continent. If two oceanic plates collide, the older, colder, and denser plate usually subducts beneath the younger plate, with an ocean trench marking the plate boundary. As a subducting plate sinks back into the mantle, water that was in the ocean crust rises into the overlying mantle, lowering its melting point. Magma forms and rises up through the overlying plate, producing volcanoes. On land, this results in the formation of volcanic mountains. Mountains can also form as ocean seafloor sediments are scraped onto the edge of the overlying plate, forming a large wedge of rock.

Under the sea, subduction produces undersea volcanoes, also known as seamounts. If they grow tall enough, these volcanoes form a volcanic island chain. This is why there are often chains of volcanic islands where convergent boundaries exist in the ocean.

Investigate Explore different plate interactions.

Collision at a Convergent Boundary

Figure 8 When two continental plates collide, their collision can have a crumpling effect on the crust that produces tall mountains, just as for two cars in a head-on collision. If one plate is denser, such as a plate of oceanic crust, that denser plate will dive under the other. This can also produce mountains as the overlying plate edge is uplifted.

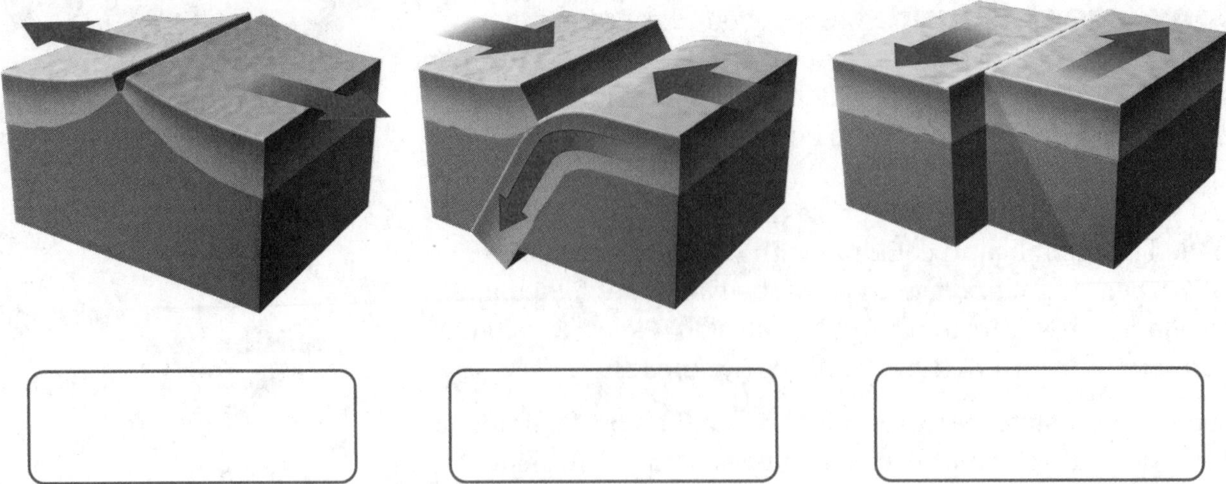

Types of Plate Boundaries

Figure 9 The three types of plate boundaries are modeled here. Label each illustration with the term that describes the boundary.

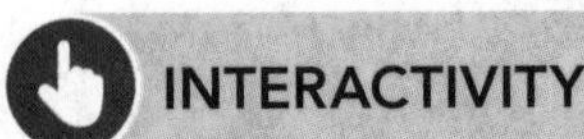

INTERACTIVITY

Investigate how stress is built up and released at faults.

Transform Boundaries Plates slide past each other at a transform boundary. Earthquakes occur here on faults called transform faults. Bending across a fault occurs when the two sides remain locked together. When enough stress builds up, the fault ruptures and an earthquake occurs. This is what causes earthquakes along transform faults such as the San Andreas Fault in California. In some cases a surface feature (such as a stream or road) that crossed a fault is visibly offset after a major slippage of the plates. Depending on how the plate edges match up, a vertical offset can exist across the fault.

Transform faults also form on the ocean floor. They cross mid-ocean ridges at right angles to form fracture zones. The result is the stepped shape of the mid-ocean ridges seen in **Figure 6**.

Keep in mind that the tectonic plates of Earth's lithosphere are three-dimensional objects that are moving around a sphere. The shapes of the plates are irregular. This means every plate has some mixture of the different types of boundaries, and at some point the boundaries may change as the plates shrink, grow, collide, slip past each other, subduct, and so on. Interactions among tectonic plates continue to reshape Earth's surface features.

CHECK POINT **Cite Textual Evidence** What happens at divergent, convergent, and transform boundaries?

LESSON 2 Check

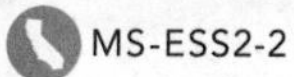

1. **Compare and Contrast** At what type of plate boundary would you find a rift valley that is growing wider?

   Divergent

2. **SEP Interpret Data** Describe what is going on in this diagram.

   This is an convergent boundries which is when two plates collide or move toward each other

3. **SEP Cause and Effect** What other surface feature that is not shown in the diagram could be produced as a result of the process shown?

4. **CCC Use Mathematics** It takes 100,000 years for a plate to move about 2 kilometers. What is that plate's rate of motion in centimeters per year? Write and solve an equation, using the variable s for speed.

5. **Connect to Nature of Science** What does the theory of plate tectonics have that Wegener's hypothesis of continental drift did not have?

Quest CHECK-IN

In this lesson, you learned about the specific mechanisms by which plates move and how interactions of tectonic plates affect Earth's surface.

SEP Construct Explanations What's the connection between Mount Rainier and the plate boundaries along the coast of the Pacific Northwest?

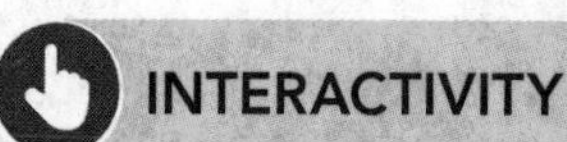

INTERACTIVITY

Mount Rainier's Threat

Go online to learn how Mount Rainier and other volcanic mountains in the Cascade Range formed as a result of geologic activity at tectonic plate boundaries.

LESSON 3

Earthquakes and Tsunami Hazards

HANDS-ON LAB

uInvestigate Analyze data and interpret patterns to predict future earthquakes.

MS-ESS2-2 Construct an explanation based on evidence for how geoscience processes have changed Earth's surface at varying time and spatial scales.

MS-ESS3-2 Analyze and interpret data on natural hazards to forecast future catastrophic events.

Connect It!

Circle the evidence that an earthquake occurred.

CCC Cause and Effect How do you think an earthquake caused this damage?

Stress and Earth's Crust

The movement of Earth's massive tectonic plates generates tremendous force. This force can bend and break the rock of Earth's crust. The force that acts on rock to change its shape or volume is called **stress**. There are three kinds of stress. **Tension** pulls on Earth's crust, stretching the rock to make it thinner, especially at the point halfway between the two pulling forces. **Compression** squeezes rock until it bends or breaks. When compression occurs at a large scale, rock can be folded into mountains. **Shearing** occurs when rock is being pushed in two opposite directions, to the point that it bends or breaks. These types of stress can produce both folds and faults. Movement of Earth's crust around faults can produce destructive earthquakes **(Figure 1)** which are internal processes, and, in some cases, tsunamis, which are surface processes.

Make Meaning As you go through the lesson, keep notes in your science notebook about how the physical stresses described here are involved in processes that produce earthquakes and tsunamis.

Earthquake Damage

Figure 1 In 1989, this two-level freeway in Oakland, California, was damaged by the Loma Prieta earthquake.

Death Valley

Figure 2 Tension can result in peaks around a sunken valley, such as Death Valley, in California.

Normal Fault A **fault** is a break in the rock of Earth's crust or mantle. Most faults occur along plate boundaries, where stress of one or more types is deforming the rock, leading to changes at Earth's surface (**Figure 2**). The two sides of a fault are referred to as walls. The wall with rock that is above the fault is called the hanging wall, and the wall that is below the fault is called the footwall. In a normal fault, the hanging wall slips down relative to the footwall (**Figure 3A**). This usually occurs at a divergent plate boundary, where tension is pulling the plates away from each other. In a normal fault, a slab of crust that falls away becomes a valley while the adjacent slab becomes mountains.

Reverse Fault Compression can produce a reverse fault, in which the hanging wall slides up and over the footwall (**Figure 3B**). The northern Rocky Mountains were gradually lifted by the action at several reverse faults. Reverse faults are common at convergent boundaries.

Strike-Slip Fault California's San Andreas Fault is a product of shearing. Walls of rock grind past each other in opposite directions, making a strike-slip fault (**Figure 3C**). Transform boundaries are home to strike-slip faults.

CHECK POINT **Determine Central Ideas** Pair each fault type with the type of stress that produces it.

....

....

Types of Faults

Figure 3 **SEP Develop Models** The three types of faults are shown here. Complete diagrams A and B by labeling the hanging walls and footwalls. In Diagram C, draw arrows to indicate the direction of shearing force and the movement along the fault.

Key

Movement along the fault

Force deforming the crust

A Normal fault

B Reverse fault

C Strike-slip fault

Valleys and Mountains

Figure 4 As tension pulls rock apart along normal faults, some blocks fall, leaving others elevated. Over time, the resulting mountains weather.

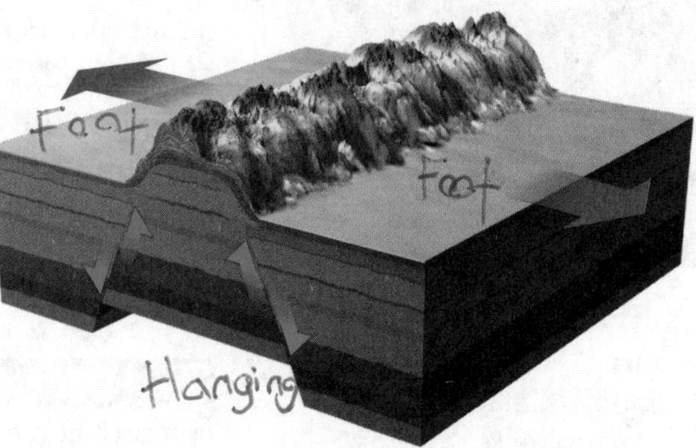

Key

 Movement along the fault

 Force deforming the crust

New Landforms From Plate Movement

Over millions of years, the forces of plate movement can change a flat plain into folded mountains, fault-block mountains, and other dramatic features of Earth's surface.

Tension and Normal Faults To see how tension and normal faults produce mountains, you need to think on a larger scale and look at a series of at least two normal faults. Where two plates move away from each other, tension forms numerous faults that run parallel to each other over a wide area. A wedge of rock that has hanging walls at both faults drops down to form a rift valley as tension pulls the adjacent footwalls away (**Figure 4**). A wedge of rock that has footwalls at both faults rises up as tension pulls the adjacent footwalls away. Mountains built this way are called *fault-block mountains.*

Folding Compression within a plate causes the crust to deform without breaking. Folds are bends in rock that form when compression shortens and thickens Earth's crust. Folds may be centimeters across or they may span many kilometers. The folds are often most visible and obvious when the rock is layered. When folding occurs on a large **scale,** folds that bend upward become mountains and folds that bend downward become valleys.

Academic Vocabulary

The processes of plate tectonics occur at different scales of time and space. List some different terms that are used to describe distance and time at vastly different scales.

....

....

....

Folded Rock

Figure 5 Formations near Palmdale, California, reveal distinct folding patterns.

Anticlines and Synclines A fold in rock that bends upward into an arch is called an anticline (AN tih klyn). This may resemble the crest of a wave, as seen in **Figure 5**. Weathering and erosion have shaped many large-scale anticlines into mountains. The height of an anticline is exaggerated by the valley-like syncline (SIN klyn), which is a fold that bends downward. This is similar to the trough of a wave. Like a series of fault-block mountains, a series of folded mountains is often marked by valleys between rows of mountains. Viewed at a large scale, a wide area of compressed crust may have mountains and valleys made of anticlines and synclines (**Figure 6**), while the large-scale folds may themselves contain their own anticlines and synclines.

CHECK POINT **Summarize Text** Describe how both compression and tension can create mountains and valleys.

....

....

....

....

Anticlines and Synclines as Mountains and Valleys

Figure 6 Label the anticlines and synclines in the diagram.

SEP Evaluate Information How does this figure oversimplify how compression produces folds in Earth's crust?

....

....

....

Earthquakes

Investigate Analyze data and interpret patterns to predict future earthquakes.

Some plate interactions are gradual, quiet, and almost imperceptible. Others can be sudden, violent, loud, and destructive. At some faults, the plates may grind to a halt and remain stuck in place for years. Stress builds up until the plates lurch into motion, releasing a great amount of energy. The shaking that results from this plate movement is an **earthquake**. Some of the energy released in an earthquake is in the form of seismic waves.

Seismic Waves Similar to sound waves, seismic waves are vibrations that travel through Earth carrying energy released by various processes, such as earthquakes, ocean storms, and volcanic eruptions. There are three types of seismic waves, as shown in **Figure 7.** The waves begin at the earthquake's focus, where rock that was under stress begins to break or move. Waves strike most quickly and with the most energy at the point on Earth's surface directly above the earthquake's focus, called the epicenter. But seismic waves also move in all directions, through and across Earth's interior and surface. When seismic waves pass from one material to another, they can change speeds and directions.

P and S Waves

Figure 7 SEP Develop Models The motion of particles in Earth's surface is shown for P waves and S waves. Draw the particle motion for the surface waves.

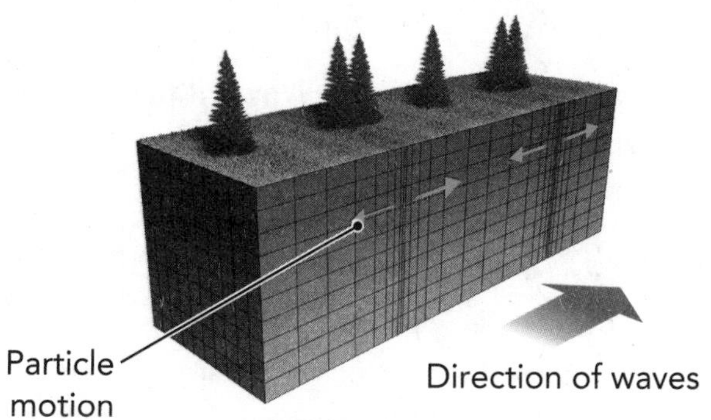

P waves, short for primary waves, travel the fastest. They are the first to arrive at a location on Earth's surface. P waves compress and expand the ground.

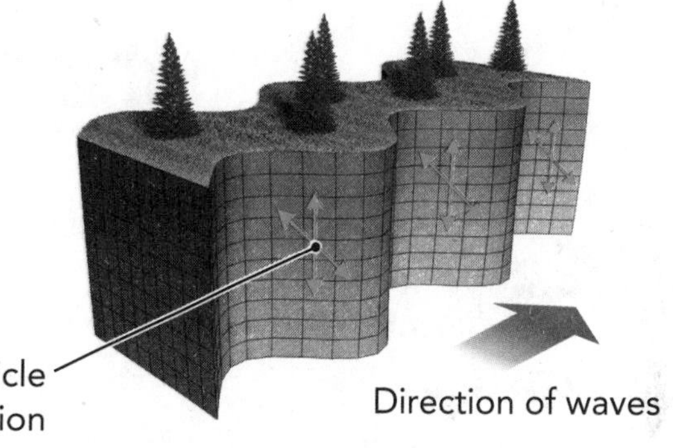

S waves, short for secondary waves, travel more slowly so they arrive after P waves. S waves can move the ground side to side or up and down.

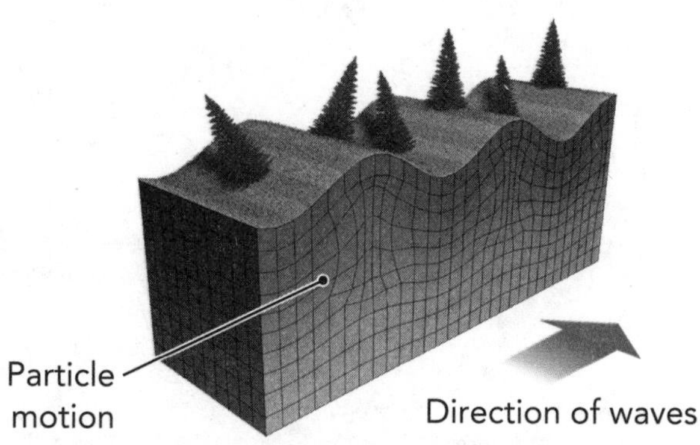

Surface waves can form when P waves and S waves reach Earth's surface. The result can be a kind of rolling motion, like ocean waves, where particles move in a pattern that is almost circular. Surface waves damage structures on the surface.

Seismogram

Figure 8 The surface waves that travel along Earth's surface usually have the largest amplitudes and therefore cause the most damage.

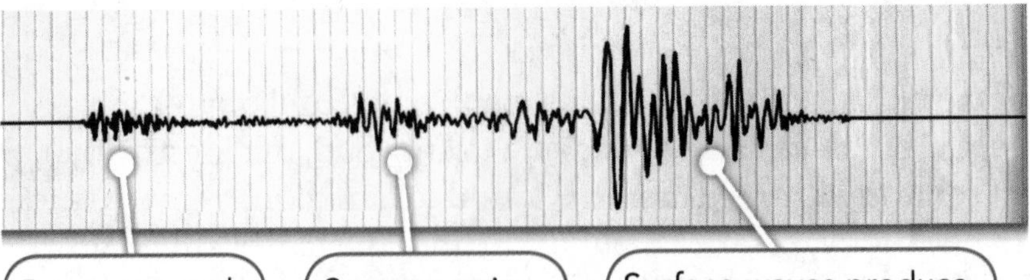

P waves travel fastest and arrive first.
S waves arrive shortly after P waves.
Surface waves produce the largest disturbance on the seismogram.

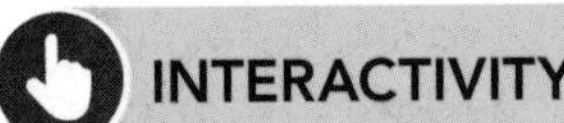

INTERACTIVITY

Analyze seismic waves to locate an earthquake.

Seismographs Seismic waves produced by earthquakes are measured by a device called a seismograph, or seismometer. This device converts the energy in the different waves to a visual called a seismogram **(Figure 8)**. The seismogram shows the timing of the different seismic waves, with the relatively gentle P and S waves arriving first, followed by surface waves with larger amplitudes. The amplitudes, or heights, of the waves on a seismogram are used to quantify the size of the earthquake.

When an earthquake occurs, geologists use data from seismograph stations in different locations to pinpoint the earthquake's epicenter (**Figure 9**). Locating the epicenter helps geologists to identify areas where earthquakes may occur in the future.

CHECK POINT **Determine Central Ideas** Why is it helpful for geologists to locate the epicenters of earthquakes?

....

....

Model It!

Triangulation

Figure 9 If you have data from three seismograph stations, you can find the precise location of an earthquake's epicenter. The center of each circle is the location of a station. The radius of each circle is the distance from the epicenter. The point where the three circles cross is the location of the epicenter.

SEP Analyze Data

Draw an X on the map to indicate the epicenter of the earthquake.

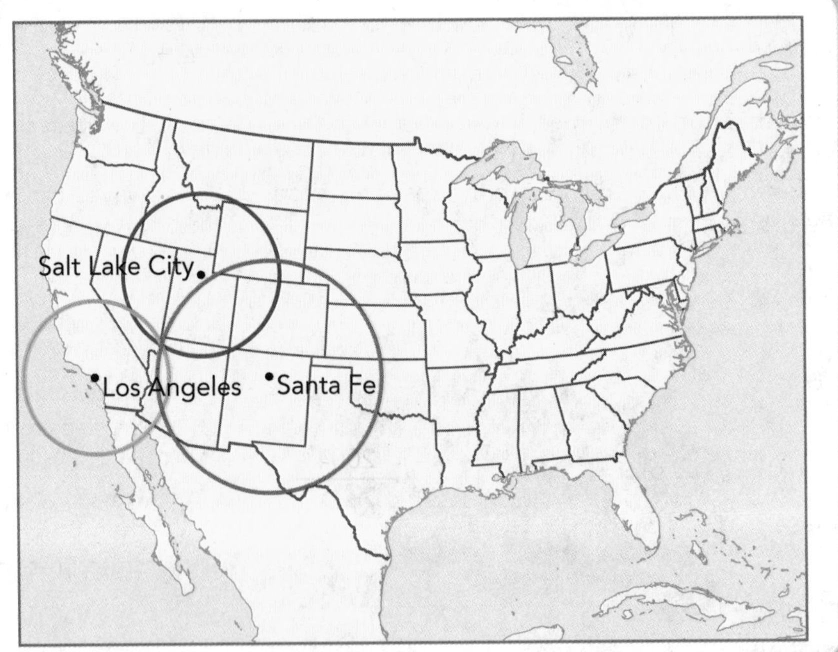

Finding an Epicenter

Geologists are trying to locate the epicenter of an earthquake. The data table below shows the arrival times of seismic waves at three different stations across Earth's surface. Use the graph to answer the questions.

Station	P Wave Arrival Time	S Wave Arrival Time	Distance from Epicenter (km)
A	4 min 6 s	7 min 25 s	
B	6 min 58 s	12 min 36 s	
C	9 min 21 s	16 min 56 s	

1. **Analyze Graphs** Use the graph to determine the distance of each station from the epicenter. Record the distance in the table.
2. **SEP Interpret Data** If another station were 5,000 km from the epicenter of the earthquake, about how long after the start of the earthquake would the S waves have arrived at this station?

P and S Waves

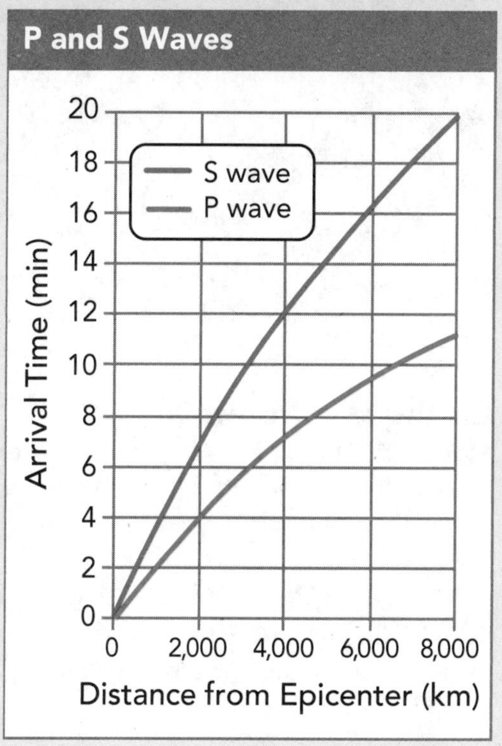

Magnitude An earthquake's **magnitude** is a single number that geologists use to assign to an earthquake based on the earthquake's size. The size of an earthquake is usually measured using the moment magnitude scale, which is a measure of the energy released. Each whole-number increase in this scale represents a roughly 32-fold increase in energy. So, the seismic waves of a magnitude-9 earthquake are 10 times larger than for a magnitude-8 earthquake. The energy released, however, is 32 times greater **(Figure 10)**. To minimize damage from large earthquakes, engineers design buildings with specialized features. Tension ties, base isolators, cross braces, and dampers are used in construction to absorb and scatter earthquake energy or support the building structure.

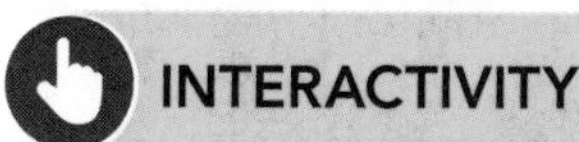

Explore technologies that help make buildings earthquake resistant.

Magnitude	Location	Date
9.2	Sumatra	2004
9.0	Japan	2011
7.9	China	2008
7.9	Nepal	2015
7.0	Haiti	2010

Earthquake Magnitude

Figure 10 The table shows the moment magnitudes of some large earthquakes.

CCC Scale, Proportion, and Quantity How much more energy was released by the earthquake in China than by the one in Haiti?

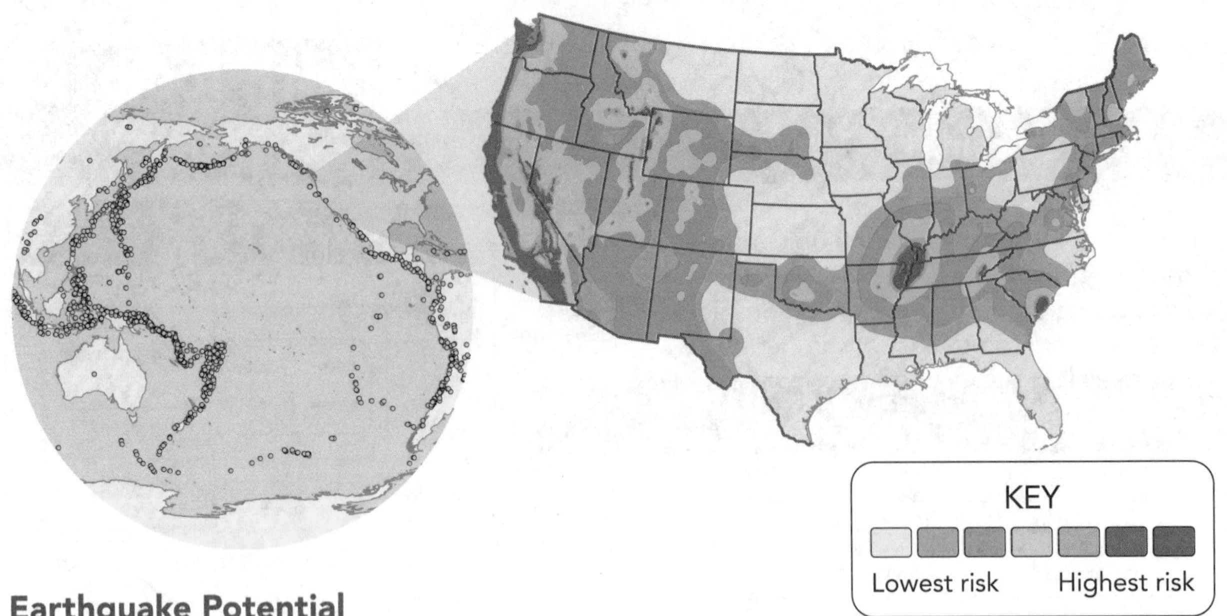

Earthquake Potential

Figure 11 The globe shows earthquakes occurring from 2007 to 2017 that were magnitude 6.0 or greater. The U.S. Geological Survey has mapped the risk of earthquakes in the United States. The risk of injury and property damage can be greatly reduced if structures follow newer building codes, such as those in California.

1. CCC Cause and Effect What do you think accounts for the higher risk of earthquakes in Los Angeles than in the middle of the U.S.?

2. Connect to Society What societal need would wider use of technology for forecasting earthquakes address?

Literacy Connection

Evaluate Media Identify an area of the U.S. earthquake risk map in **Figure 11** that does not fit the pattern of earthquake occurrences described on this page. Circle the area. California has its own maps of earthquake risk zones.

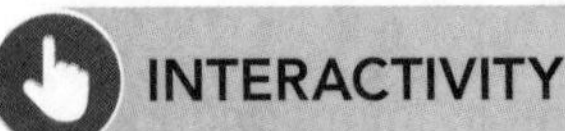

Help determine the best location for a new stadium in an earthquake zone.

Earthquake Risks and Tsunamis

The "Ring of Fire" around the Pacific Ocean is where many of the world's earthquakes occur. There are many plate boundaries around the Pacific, including convergent and transform boundaries where stress builds up. Because the west coast of the United States, including Alaska, is on the edge of several boundaries, the western states have a much higher risk of experiencing an earthquake than other regions of the United States, as shown in **Figure 11**. Earthquakes themselves can cause tremendous damage, but if they occur near or below the ocean floor, they can produce another type of disaster.

Ocean Floor Uplift When an area of Earth's crust moves during an earthquake, it forces anything above it to move as well. For example, an area of off-shore ocean floor that has been stressed for years at a convergent plate boundary can suddenly pop up, thrusting up the ocean water above it. Depending on how the water is moved, a tsunami may form.

A **tsunami** is a wave or series of waves produced by an earthquake or landslide. Unlike typical ocean waves formed by the wind, tsunami waves can involve the entire water column—every drop between the surface and the ocean floor. That means they can carry tremendous energy and can be highly destructive **(Figure 12)**. Engineers have developed technologies that record seismic data and sea level changes in the deep ocean, such as tsunami detection buoys, are used in tsunami warning systems to minimize damage and loss of life. If there is a tsunami threat, alerts can be sent via television and radio stations, and some mobile devices. Warning siren systems can also transmit alerts by using different sounds to indicate a tsunami threat, the need to evacuate, or if the threat has passed.

A Wall of Water

Figure 12 A tsunami does not always look like a wave. In some cases it is just a sudden, massive rise in sea level, which simply floods low-lying areas.

Landslides Ocean floor uplift is one cause of tsunamis. Landslides are another. In both cases, some kind of displacement of water occurs, setting the tsunami in motion. In 1958, an earthquake triggered a landslide on a mountainside on the shore of Lituya Bay, Alaska. About 30 million cubic meters of rock tumbled into the water at one end of the bay, producing a tsunami that swept across the bay and splashed as high as 524 meters up along the steep shoreline **(Figure 13)**.

CHECK POINT **Cite Textual Evidence** How can an earthquake or landslide produce a tsunami?

....

....

....

Tsunami Hazards

Figure 13 The site of the rockslide that produced the tsunami in Lituya Bay is marked by the circle.

SEP Cite Evidence Draw lines to indicate where the water splashed up and tore away plants and sediment from the bay's shore.

LESSON 3 Check

MS-ESS2-2, MS-ESS3-2

1. **Identify** Which type of stress on Earth's crust can make a slab of rock shorter and thicker?

Compression

2. **SEP Construct Explanations** How do mountains and valleys form through folding?

3. **Explain Phenomena** You hear about a magnitude 8.0 earthquake on the news. Someone says "That doesn't sound too bad. An 8.0 is just one more than the 7.0 we had here last year." Explain why that's not the right way to think about the moment magnitude scale.

4. **SEP Design Solutions** What technologies have engineers developed to reduce the effects of a natural hazard?

5. **CCC Stability and Change** Describe the role that stress plays in the production of earthquakes and tsunamis.

Quest CHECK-IN

In this lesson, you learned about the connection between plate tectonics and features and events at Earth's surface, including mountains and earthquakes.

Evaluate How can monitoring Earth for seismic activity near plate boundaries be useful in monitoring volcanoes?

INTERACTIVITY

Monitoring a Volcano

Go online to practice several data collection and analysis techniques to monitor a volcano and predict an eruption.

littleBits™

MS-ESS3-2

DESIGNING TO PREVENT Destruction

VIDEO

Watch how underwater earthquakes displace water.

How do you design a building that can withstand the forceful waves of a tsunami? You engineer it!

The Challenge: To construct tsunami-safe buildings.

Though much smaller than the one that struck Japan in 2011, a 1964 tsunami devastated Crescent City, California, shown above.

Phenomenon A seafloor earthquake can displace water above it, causing a tsunami to form. When the tsunami reaches land, giant waves cause widespread destruction.

Because parts of the United States are at risk for tsunamis, U.S. engineers have developed new building standards to save lives and mitigate the damage. They studied new design concepts. Strong columns enable buildings to stand, even when battered by tons of water and debris. Exits on upper floors allow people to get out when lower floors are flooded.

To develop standards, engineers visited Japan, where an earthquake and tsunami in 2011 caused terrible losses of life and property. The engineers also used wave research to model tsunamis and their impact on buildings.

These engineers hope that hospitals, schools, and police stations, if built to the new standards, can then provide shelter for people fleeing danger.

It is a challenge to design and engineer structures that can withstand the force of a tsunami. Under new standards, schools would be built to withstand the force of water and debris. This increases the cost of construction, but the improved safety far outweighs the added cost.

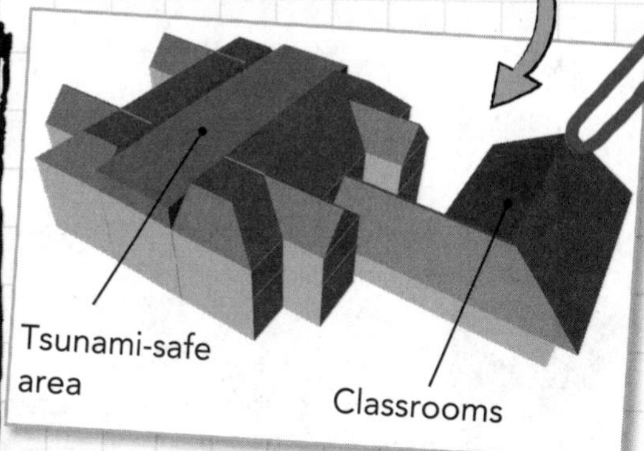

DESIGN CHALLENGE Can you design a structure that will withstand the force of a tsunami? Go to the Engineering Design Notebook to find out!

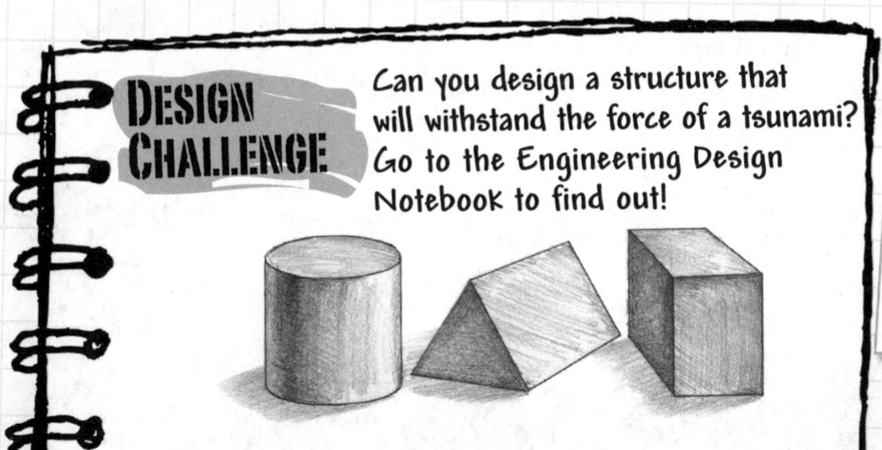

Volcanoes and Earth's Surface

HANDS-ON LAB

uInvestigate Explore moving volcanoes.

MS-ESS2-2 Construct an explanation based on evidence for how geoscience processes have changed Earth's surface at varying time and spatial scales.

MS-ESS3-2 Analyze and interpret data on natural hazards to forecast future catastrophic events. (Also **EP&CIb**)

Connect It!

Circle and label effects that the volcano in the photo is having on Earth's surface and atmosphere.

CCC Systems List the effects that you identified in the photo, and categorize them by the Earth system that is affected—hydrosphere, atmosphere, geosphere, biosphere.

Volcanoes

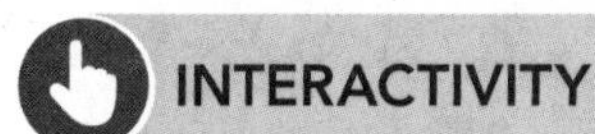

Explore how an erupting volcano might change Earth's surface.

While active volcanoes are found in a relatively small number of states in the United States, they have a profound effect on Earth's surface—especially at plate boundaries. Volcanoes add new material to Earth's surface, release gases into the atmosphere, build new islands, shape habitats for organisms and enrich soil with volcanic ash. A **volcano** is a structure that forms in Earth's crust when molten material, or magma, reaches Earth's surface. This can occur on land or on the ocean floor. **Magma** is a molten mixture of rock-forming substances, gases, and water from the mantle. Once magma reaches the surface, it is known as **lava**. When lava cools, it forms solid rock.

As with earthquakes, there is a pattern to where volcanoes occur on Earth. Most are found at convergent or divergent plate boundaries, but they can also occur at seemingly random places far from plate boundaries.

Volcanism

Figure 1 The activity of volcanoes is called volcanism. Eruptions that release lava and other matter from Earth's interior can pose hazards to organisms, including humans. The natural system of volcanism also provides benefits for ecosystems.

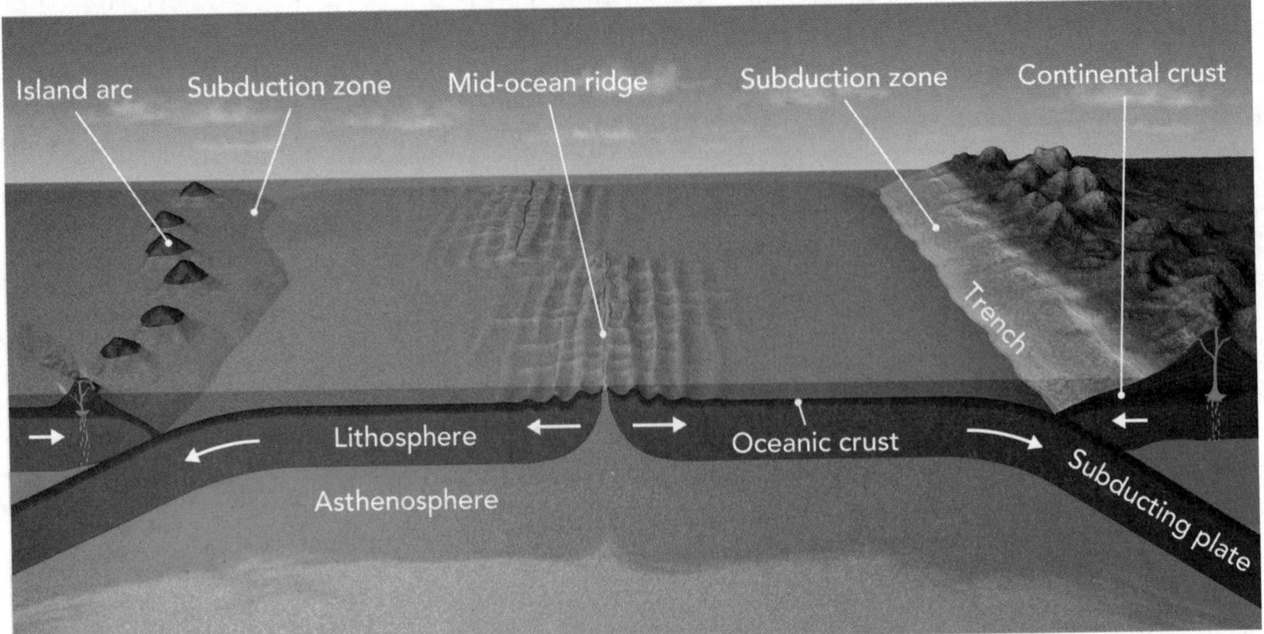

Divergent and Convergent Boundaries

Figure 2 Volcanic activity at plate boundaries can produce volcanoes on continents and volcanic island arcs.

SEP Construct Explanations Describe what is happening on the left side of the diagram, where ash is rising in the air over an active volcano.

Volcanoes and Plate Boundaries

At convergent boundaries, the subduction of an oceanic plate under a continental plate can produce volcanoes along the edge of the continent. Subduction of an oceanic plate under an adjacent oceanic plate can result in a volcanic island arc. At divergent boundaries, molten magma comes through the crust as lava, which quickly hardens into rock, but if the volume of magma is especially large, then a volcanic cone may form. **Figure 2** summarizes these processes.

At Divergent Boundaries Volcanoes form at divergent boundaries when plates move apart and rock rises to fill the vacant space. Most volcanoes at divergent boundaries occur in the ocean at mid-ocean ridges, so they are never seen. Only in places such as Iceland can you see ocean-ridge volcanoes. Less common are volcanoes, like Mt. Kilimanjaro, that occur at continental divergent boundaries such as the East African Rift.

At Convergent Boundaries When a plate dives into the mantle in the process of subduction, trapped water leaves the sinking plate and mixes with the material of the overlying mantle, causing it to melt. The buoyant magma starts to rise toward the surface. If the magma reaches the surface before cooling, a volcano forms. If the overlying plate is part of the ocean floor, the resulting volcano begins to form on the seafloor as a seamount. If it grows large enough to break the ocean surface, it becomes a volcanic island. A chain of islands may form when volcanism occurs at multiple spots along the edge of an oceanic plate. This is called a volcanic island arc.

Investigate Explore moving volcanoes.

Hot Spot Volcanism In addition to divergent and convergent plate boundaries, there is a third source of volcanoes: hot spots. A **hot spot** is an area where lava frequently erupts at the surface, independent of plate boundary processes. Most hot spots sit atop mantle plumes of hot rock. Hot spot plumes are fixed within the deep mantle. As a plate moves over the plume, a chain of volcanoes is created because older volcanoes keep being carried away from the hot spot. The many islands and seamounts of Hawaii have formed from the westward motion of the Pacific Plate, as is illustrated in **Figure 3**. Another hot spot is found at Yellowstone National Park in Wyoming. The "supervolcano" beneath the park may erupt again someday. During past giant eruptions of Yellowstone, the last one being 640,000 years ago, most of North America was covered with volcanic ash.

Learn more about volcanology.

CHECK POINT **Determine Conclusions** The Aleutian Islands of Alaska form a chain near a plate boundary. What type of boundary is it?

....

Model It!

Hot Spot Modeling

Figure 3 The Hawaiian Islands have formed from the movement of the Pacific Plate over a hot spot plume.

Integrate with Visuals

Using the diagram as inspiration, design a functioning physical model of how a hot spot makes volcanoes on the ocean crust of a moving plate. Sketch or describe your model in the space here, including details on how it would work. Explain what became clear from working on the model that was not clear from your reading.

Composite Volcano

Figure 4 A composite volcano has alternating layers of hardened lava and ash.

SEP Develop Models Complete the diagram by reading the description of the volcano's parts and writing in the missing labels.

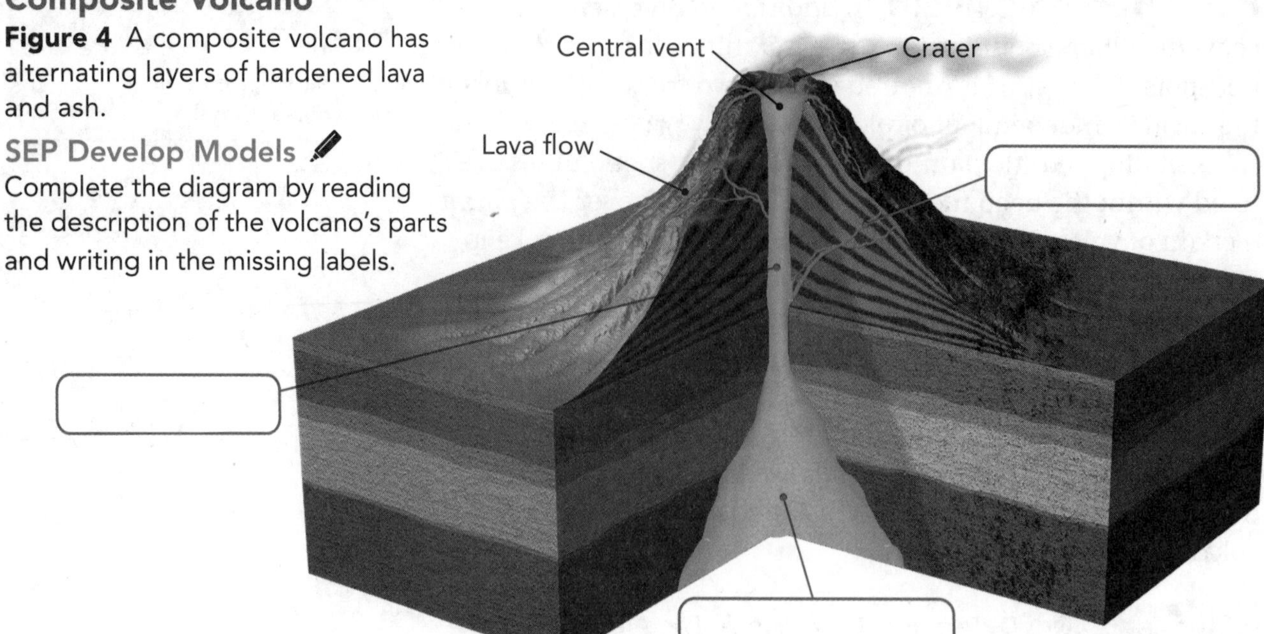

Literacy Connection

Integrate with Visuals Use the diagram of the volcano to help you understand the text on this page.

Volcano Landforms

Magma usually forms in the layer of hot rock in the upper mantle. Because magma is less dense than the rock around it, it moves upward to the surface. Once the magma exits a volcano and is exposed to air or water, it is called lava.

Volcano Parts Inside a volcano (**Figure 4**) is a system of passageways through which magma travels. Below the volcano is a magma chamber, where magma collects before an eruption. The volcano and surrounding landscape may swell slightly as the magma chamber fills. Magma moves up from the chamber through a pipe, which leads to the central vent—an opening at the top, which may be in a bowl-shaped crater. Some volcanoes have side vents, too. When lava flows out from a vent, it begins to cool and harden as it is pulled by gravity down the slope of the volcano. If lava is thrown explosively into the air, it hardens and falls to Earth in different forms. Bombs are large chunks of hardened lava. Cinders are the size of pebbles. The finest particles are called ash. The type of lava-based material that emerges from a new volcano defines the type of volcano that is built.

Academic Vocabulary

Composite refers to something made of a mixture of different parts or elements. Many manufactured objects are made of composites—blends of different raw materials. How does this help you to understand what a composite volcano is?

....

....

....

....

Volcano Types The volcano in **Figure 4** is a **composite** volcano. Also called a stratovolcano, it is made of alternating layers of lava flows and ash falls. These tend to be cone-shaped and tall. Mount Fuji in Japan is an example of a composite volcano. Other types of volcanic formations are shown in **Figure 5**.

Volcanic Formations

Figure 5 Volcanic activity can result in different landforms.

1. **Compare and Contrast** How are shield volcanoes and lava plateaus similar? How are they different?

2. **SEP Develop Models** ✎ Review the three steps of caldera formation. Finish the sentence to describe the second phase of caldera formation.

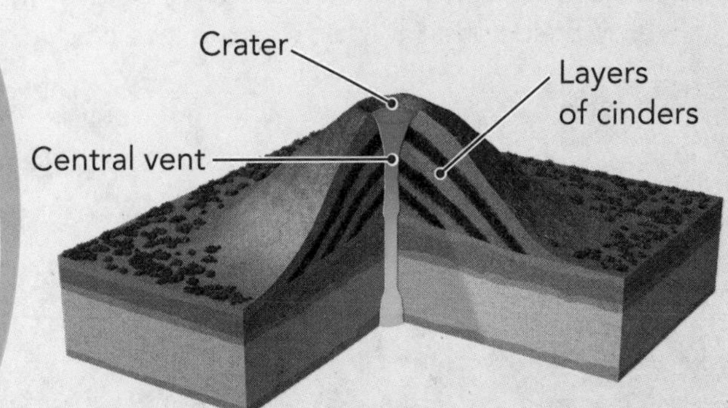

Cinder Cone Volcano If lava emerges from a new vent in Earth's crust as a mix of bombs, ash, and cinders, these materials build up into a cinder cone volcano. The loose, ashy material tends to erode quickly.

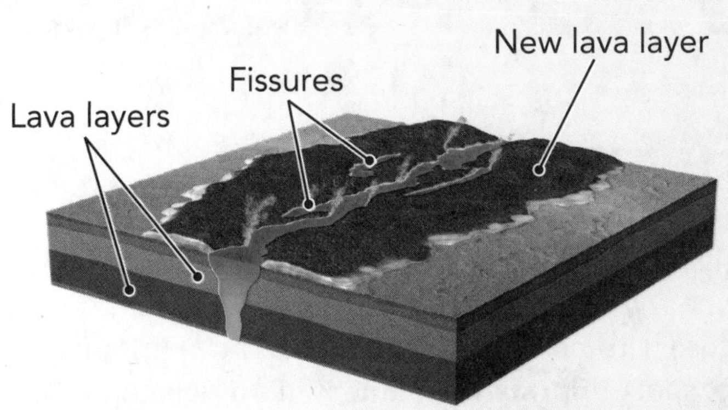

Lava Plateau Lava can flow out of several long cracks in Earth's crust and flood an area repeatedly over many years. Over time, these relatively flat layers of hardened lava build up into a lava plateau.

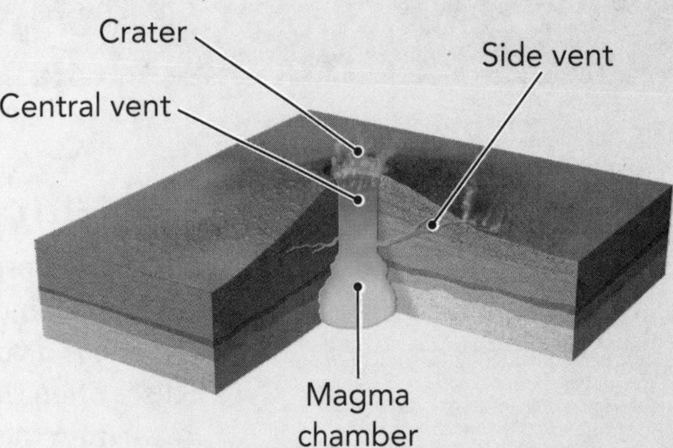

Shield Volcano Some volcanoes have slow, steady eruptions in which lava flows out and builds up over a broad area. Hot spot volcanoes tend to be shield volcanoes, and they can be massive.

Caldera A caldera forms when a volcano collapses on itself.

1. Large eruptions empty the main vent and magma chamber of the volcano.
2. Lacking support, ...
3. A lake fills the caldera. Later eruptions form a small cone.

Lava from Quiet Eruptions

Figure 6 The content and consistency of lava determines the type of rock that will form as the lava cools.

INTERACTIVITY

Explore different volcanic landforms.

Volcano Hazards

Volcanoes pose different hazards to humans and other organisms, mainly through eruptions. An **extinct**, or dead, volcano is a volcano that poses very little threat of eruption. This is often the case with hot-spot volcanoes that have drifted away from the hot spot. A **dormant** volcano is like a sleeping volcano—it poses little threat, but it could reawaken someday. **Active** volcanoes are the more immediate threat. Volcanologists classify eruptions as quiet or explosive. Whether an eruption is quiet or explosive depends in part on the magma's silica content and whether the magma is thin and runny or thick and sticky. Temperature helps determine how runny magma is.

Academic Vocabulary

What does it mean if you have an active lifestyle?

....

....

....

Quiet Eruptions If the magma in a volcano's magma chamber is hot or low in silica, it will erupt quietly. The lava will be thin and runny, and trapped gases will bubble out gently. The consistency of the lava that emerges during a quiet eruption will affect how it looks and feels when it cools, as shown in **Figure 6**. Lava that is cooler and thicker, and moves slower forms rock with a rough surface consisting of jagged lava chunks. Fast-moving, hot lava that is thin and runny, forms rock that looks like a solid mass of ropelike coils.

The Hawaiian Islands continue to be produced mostly by quiet eruptions. Quiet eruptions are not necessarily safe. For example, the Hawaii Volcanoes National Park's visitors center was threatened in 1989 by a lava flow from Mount Kilauea.

Explosive Eruptions Magma that has a large amount of silica will erupt more than magma containing little or no silica. High-silica magma is thick and sticky, causing it to build up in a pipe until pressure is so great that it bursts out over the surface. Trapped gases explode out instead of bubbling out gently. An explosion with that much force can hurl lava, ash, cinders, and bombs high into the atmosphere.

Krakatau, a volcano in a large volcanic arc in Indonesia, erupted in 1883. The eruption, depicted in **Figure 7**, was so violent that much of the the visible part of the island collapsed into the sea, producing a tsunami that killed 36,000 people. Gas and debris billowed more than 25 kilometers into the sky, and the sound from the explosion was heard 4,500 kilometers away. So much ash and sulfur dioxide was emitted into the atmosphere by the eruption that global temperatures were cooler for the following five years.

Krakatau Explodes

Figure 7 The eruption of Krakatau was a major disaster in Indonesia, but it affected the entire world as ash and sulfur dioxide entered the atmosphere.

Magma Composition

Magma is classified according to the amount of silica it contains. The less silica the magma contains, the more easily it flows. More silica makes magma stickier and thicker. Trapped gases can't emerge easily, so eruptions are explosive.

Types of Magma

Low-Silica: Silica 50%; Other oxides 47.5%; All other solids 2.5%

High-Silica: Silica 70%; Other oxides 27.5%; All other solids 2.5%

1. **Analyze Proportional Relationships** How do the two magma types compare in terms of silica content?

2. **SEP Construct Explanations** Which of the magma types would erupt more explosively? How would knowing the type of magma a volcano produces help nearby communities prepare for eruptions?

Measuring Gas Concentration

Figure 8 This device, called a spectrometer, can measure concentrations of volcanic gases by measuring how light passes through them. A high concentration of sulfur dioxide may mean an eruption is likely to occur.

Predicting Volcano Hazards

Predicting Volcano Hazards Volcanologists use different tools to monitor volcanoes and predict eruptions. The gas emissions from volcanoes can be monitored to check for increases in sulfur dioxide, which may indicate that an eruption is coming **(Figure 8)**. Seismographs can detect rumblings deep inside a volcano that precede an eruption.

Volcanologists can also use devices to measure whether a volcano is swelling as its magma chamber fills up. These devices, called tiltmeters, are like carpenters' levels that detect very slight changes in the tilt of a volcano's slopes. If the tilt increases, it means the volcano is swelling and is likely to erupt. Telecommunications technology can transmit the data from these devices to scientists, who can then interpret the data and look for patterns associated with eruptions and notify the public if an eruption is predicted.

In areas with known volcanic hazards, engineering solutions, such as placing artificial barriers to divert lava and mudflows, may be utilized to help reduce the effects of an eruption. Public utilities, such as electricity, are also impacted during eruptions. To reduce the effects and maintain power to local communities, some utility companies are investigating ways to redesign their wooden utility poles to protect them from the extreme heat.

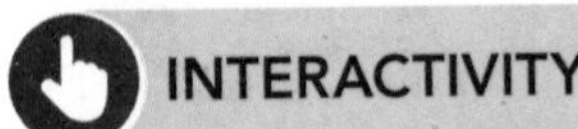

INTERACTIVITY

Analyze how volcanic activity can change Earth's surface.

CHECK POINT **Cite Textual Evidence** If sulfur dioxide concentrations emitted from a volcano increase from less than one part per million (ppm) to 4 ppm, is the volcano more or less likely to erupt soon?

....

....

Question It!

Building on a Volcano

In some parts of the world, building on a volcano is a necessity because most of the land is volcanic. Suppose you had to build a home on a volcanic island. **SEP Ask Questions** What questions would you want to answer before choosing a specific site for construction?

....

....

....

....

....

....

....

LESSON 4 Check

MS-ESS2-2, MS-ESS3-2

1. **Identify Phenomena** Runny lava oozes from the vent of a broad, gently-sloping shield volcano. What type of eruption is this?

   Quiet Eruptions

2. **SEP Construct Explanations** Why do volcanoes form at divergent and convergent boundaries?

   Volcanoes form at divergent boundaries when plates move apart and volcanoes form at convergent boundaries when the plate melts when the plate dives down into the mantle

3. **CCC Patterns** The Hawaiian Islands formed as the Pacific Plate moved west-northwest over a hot spot. In which part of the islands would you expect to find the most active volcanoes? Dormant and extinct volcanoes? Explain.

4. **SEP Interpret Data** You are sailing in the South Pacific Ocean, far from any plate boundary. Looming on the horizon is a dark, broad, rounded island with sparse vegetation. A few thin flows of orange lava drip into the sea. Some smoky vapor unfurls from the center of the island. What kind of volcano is this? Explain.

5. **CCC Structure and Function** How are volcanic island arcs formed?

Quest CHECK-IN

In this lesson, you learned about the connection between plate tectonics and volcanoes.

SEP Analyze Data Why is it important to understand the type of volcano Mount Rainier is and the patterns of activity at the nearest plate boundary?

HANDS-ON LAB

Signs of Eruption?

Go online to download the lab and identify signs of a volcanic eruption.

TOPIC 8 Review and Assess

MS-ESS2-2, MS-ESS3-2

Evidence-Based Assessment

In 2011, a magnitude 9.0 earthquake occurred in the ocean floor off the east coast of Japan. Tsunameter buoys and tide gauges recorded tsunami waves as they crossed the Pacific Ocean. Scientists used the data to predict how large the waves would be and when they would arrive at different locations. The map shown represents the tsunami forecast model for the event, which was used by coastal communities around the Pacific to prepare for local impacts of the tsunami.

Analyze the map of the 2011 tsunami wave forecast. Keep in mind the following information:

- The triangles symbolize specific tsunameter buoys, which measure wave height, or amplitude.
- The numbered contour lines represent how many hours after the earthquake the tsunami waves were forecast to reach those areas of the ocean.
- Major plate boundaries are indicated on the map.

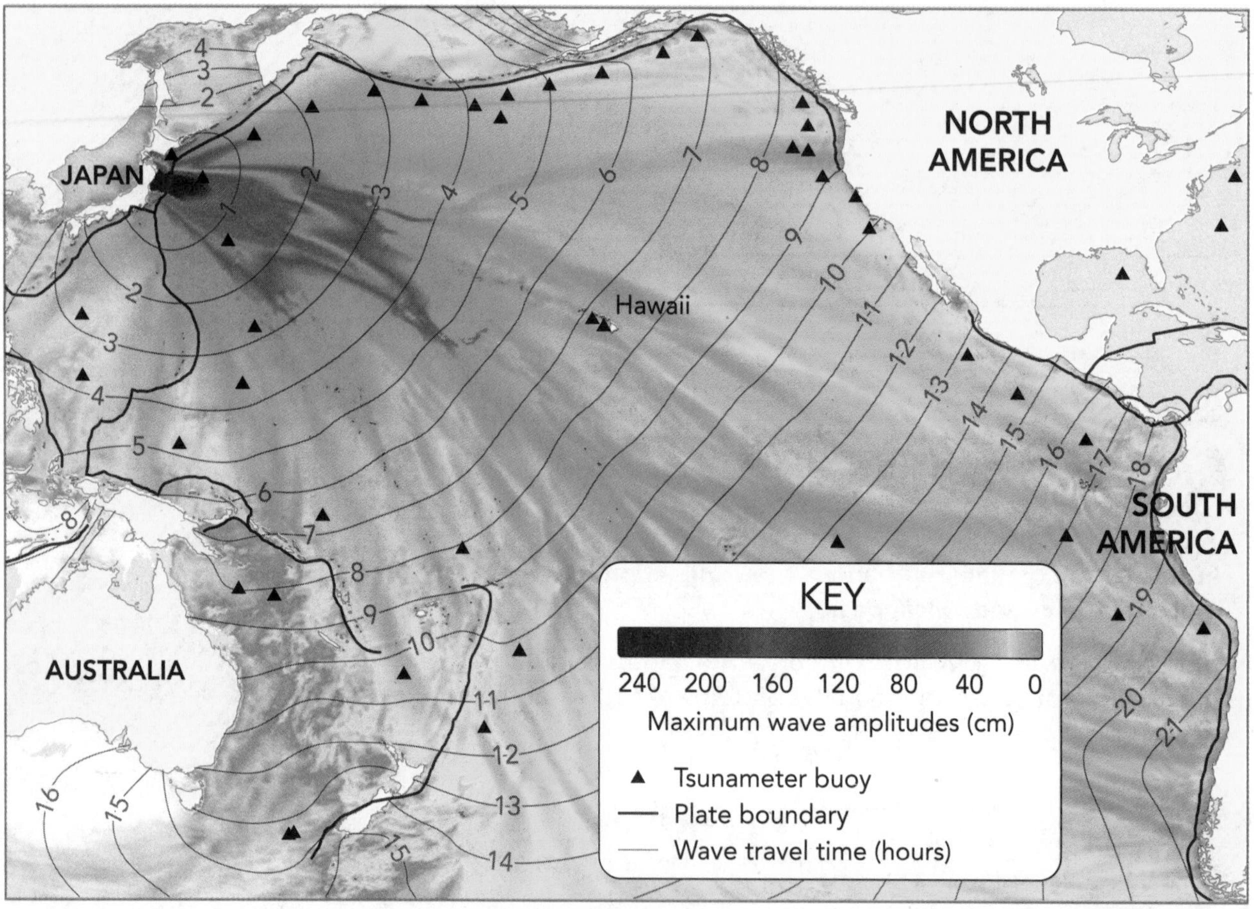

1. SEP Analyze Data According to the data, where was tsunami wave height expected to be greatest?
   A. Australia
   B. Japan
   C. North America
   D. South America

2. SEP Interpret Data What can you observe about the impact of the earthquake on Australia? Select all that apply.
   - [x] The tsunami waves reached Australia about 9 hours after the earthquake.
   - [ ] Maximum wave amplitude was between 80 cm and 120 cm.
   - [ ] Tsunami waves reached Australia and Hawaii at the same time.
   - [ ] Australia was not impacted by the earthquake in Japan.
   - [x] Tsunami waves hit Australia about 10 hours before they hit South America.

3. Model Phenomena When was the tsunami expected to reach northern California, and what was the expected wave height?
   The tsunami was expected to reach northern California in 9 hours and the height wave is about 40 something

4. CCC Cause and Effect Arrange the following events in order from 1 to 5 to describe how the motion of tectonic plates can result in a tsunami, with 1 being the first event and 5 being the last.

Events	Order
A tsunami is formed and can impact surrounding areas.	5
Tectonic plates move toward each other for long periods of time.	1
Energy lifts a large volume of water.	4
Two plates at a fault slip and release the energy, causing an earthquake.	3
Stress builds up at a fault under the water.	2

5. SEP Construct Explanations In terms of their usefulness to society in protecting human lives, why are so many tsunameters placed along coastlines of the Pacific Ocean? Provide two explanations for this use of new technology.

Quest FINDINGS

Complete the Quest!

Present information on Mount Rainier's history and current geological research, along with your evidence-based argument about whether it is safe to hike and camp there.

Reason Quantitatively What data will help you to predict whether Mount Rainier could erupt while you are on a two-week camping trip nearby? Explain.

INTERACTIVITY

Reflect on Mount Rainier's Safety

MS-ESS2-2, MS-ESS3-2

Modeling Sea-Floor Spreading

How can you prevent a major oil spill by **designing** and building a model that **demonstrates** sea-floor spreading?

Background

Phenomenon Imagine you are a marine geologist reviewing a plan to construct an undersea oil pipeline. You notice that part of the pipeline will cross a mid-ocean ridge. In this investigation, you will design and build a model that demonstrates sea-floor spreading to show why this plan is not a good idea.

Materials

(per group)
- scissors
- transparent tape
- colored pencil or marker
- metric ruler
- 2 sheets of unlined letter-sized paper
- manila folder

Safety

Be sure to follow all safety guidelines provided by your teacher. The Safety Appendix of your textbook provides more details about the safety icons.

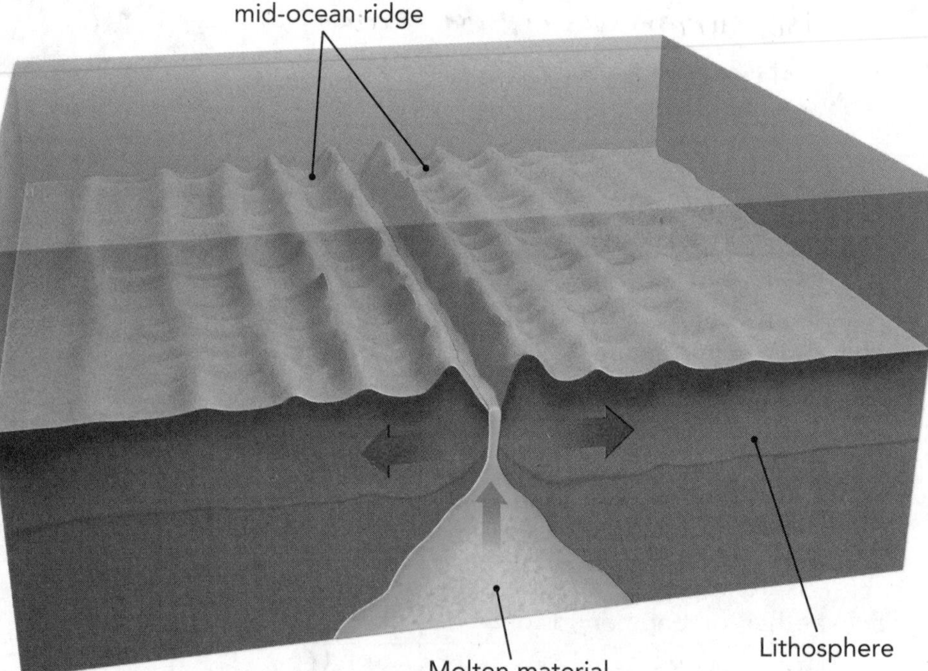

Design Your Model and Investigation

Discuss with your group why building a pipeline that spans a mid-ocean ridge is a bad idea. Over time, what will happen to the pipeline?

With your group, take a look at the materials. How can you use the materials to construct a model that demonstrates why the pipeline plan is a problem?

HANDS-ON LAB

Demonstrate Go online for a downloadable worksheet of this lab.

Consider the following questions:

- How can you use the manila folder to represent the mantle?
- How can you use the two pieces of plain letter-sized paper to create matching strips of striped sea floor?
- How can you represent the mid-ocean ridge and the subduction zones on either side of the ridge?

Use the space provided to sketch your group's model and write notes for guiding its construction. Have your teacher approve your group's plan, and then construct and demonstrate the model.

Sketch of Model

Design Notes

Analyze and Interpret Data

1. **SEP Develop Models** Why is it important that your model have identical patterns of stripes on both sides of the center slit?

2. **SEP Construct Explanations** Use evidence from your model to support the claim that sea-floor spreading builds two different tectonic plates.

3. **SEP Refine Your Solution** Look at the models created by other groups. How are the other solutions different? How might you revise your group's model to better demonstrate sea-floor spreading? Think of how your own and other class models improved your understanding of sea-floor spreading after you completed reading the lessons.

4. **SEP Use Models** How could your group revise the model to reinforce the idea that the amount of crust that forms at the mid-ocean ridge is equal to the amount of crust recycled back into the mantle at subduction zones?

5. **CCC Stability and Change** How does your model support the claim that building an oil pipeline across a divergent boundary would be a bad idea? What effects might there be on marine ecosystems?

TOPIC

9

Earth's Surface Systems

How did this rock get its strange shape?

Investigative Phenomenon

What evidence is there to explain how geoscience processes have changed Earth's surface over time?

MS-ESS2-2 Construct an explanation based on evidence for how geoscience processes have changed Earth's surface at varying time and spatial scales.

MS-ESS3-1 Construct a scientific explanation based on evidence for how the uneven distributions of Earth's mineral, energy, and groundwater resources are the result of past and current geoscience processes.

MS-ESS3-2 Analyze and interpret data on natural hazards to forecast future catastrophic events and inform the development of technologies to mitigate their effects.

EP&CIc Students should be developing an understanding that the quality, quantity and reliability of the goods and ecosystem services provided by natural systems are directly affected by the health of those systems.

EP&CIIIa Students should be developing an understanding that natural systems proceed through cycles and processes that are required for their functioning.

EP&CIIIb Students should be developing an understanding that human practices depend upon and benefit from the cycles and processes that operate within natural systems.

HANDS-ON LAB

uConnect Explore how the height and width of a hill affects mass movement.

What questions do you have about the phenomenon?

Quest PBL

How can I design and build an artificial island?

STEM **Figure It Out** One way to expand a city surrounded by water is to make more land. Parts of San Francisco, such as Mission Bay, were constructed on landfill, rubble from the 1906 earthquake, and sand dredged from the bay. But what factors do engineers need to consider when they create new land in the middle of water? In this problem-based Quest activity, you will design an artificial island that can withstand nature's forces and that has minimal environmental impact.

INTERACTIVITY

Ingenious Islands

MS-ESS2-2, MS-ESS3-2, EP&CIc

After watching the Quest Kickoff video about how coastal engineers study and reduce coastal erosion, complete the 3-2-1 activity.

3 ways that water changes land

....

....

....

2 ways that wind changes land

....

....

1 way that those changes could be prevented or minimized

....

....

Quest CHECK-IN

IN LESSON 1

How does weathering affect various materials? Consider the benefits and drawbacks of using different materials for an artificial island.

HANDS-ON LAB

Breaking It Down

Quest CHECK-INS

IN LESSON 2

STEM What criteria and constraints need to be considered when designing your island model to resist erosion over periods of time? Design and build your island model.

HANDS-ON LAB

Ingenious Island: Part I

INTERACTIVITY

Changing Landscapes

Quest CHECK-IN

IN LESSON 3

STEM How resistant is your island model to erosion? Test the effects of the agents of erosion on your model and make improvements.

HANDS-ON LAB

Ingenious Island: Part II

Beachfront properties line one of the "branches" of the Palm Jumeirah in the United Arab Emirates. The palm-shaped artificial island extends into the Persian Gulf off the coast of Dubai. It provides miles of additional shoreline for homes and elaborate hotels.

Quest CHECK-IN

IN LESSON 4

How can wave erosion impact the location of your artificial island? Adjust your design as needed to account for wave erosion.

INTERACTIVITY

Breaking Waves

IN LESSON 5

How can rain and the flooding that may result from severe weather impact erosion? Consider this when finalizing your design.

Quest FINDINGS

Complete the Quest!

Present your island model and explain how your design decisions relate to the forces that change Earth's surface.

INTERACTIVITY

Reflect on Your Ingenious Island

LESSON 1

Weathering and Soil

HANDS-ON LAB

uInvestigate Look at how ice helps to break down rock.

MS-ESS2-2 Construct an explanation based on evidence for how geoscience processes have changed Earth's surface at varying time and spatial scales.

MS-ESS3-1 Construct a scientific explanation based on evidence for how the uneven distributions of Earth's mineral, energy, and groundwater resources are the result of past and current geoscience processes. (Also **EP&CIc**)

Connect It!

Sometimes called cheeserock, spectacular Tafoni formations can be found along California's long coastline. Circle an area on the rock where material has been removed.

SEP **Construct Explanations** What processes produced the pattern in the rock?

Breaking Down Earth's Surface

Even the hardest rocks wear down over time on Earth's surface. Natural processes, such as the one that produced the rock formation in **Figure 1**, break down rocks and carry the pieces away. Geologists make inferences about what processes shaped Earth's surface in the past based on the **principle** of **uniformitarianism** (yoon uh form uh TAYR ee un iz um). This principle states that the geoscience processes that operate today also operated in the past. Scientists infer that ancient landforms and features formed through the same processes they observe today and will continue to do so in the future.

The processes of weathering and erosion (ee ROH zhun) work together to change Earth's surface by wearing down and carrying away rock particles. The process of weathering breaks down rock and other substances. Heat, cold, water, ice, and gases all contribute to weathering. **Erosion** involves the removal of rock particles by wind, water, ice, or gravity.

Weathering and erosion work continuously to reshape Earth's surface. The same processes that wear down mountains over scales that are vast in space and long in time also cause bicycles to rust, paint to peel, and sidewalks to crack on scales that are small and brief. Weathering and erosion can take millions of years to break down and wear away huge mountains, or they can take seconds to carry rock away in an avalanche. These geoscience processes started changing Earth's surface billions of years ago and they continue to do so.

VIRTUAL LAB

Explore one factor that affects the time it takes weathering to occur.

Academic Vocabulary

Describe another principle you follow in science or in your everyday life.

....

....

....

Determine Meaning

How has weathering or erosion affected you? In your science notebook, describe an example of weathering or erosion you observed and any impact it had on you or your community.

California Cheeserock

Figure 1 Several processes produce the honeycomb-like holes in this coastal rock found in Salt Point State Park near Jenner, California.

Mechanical Weathering

Figure 2 Label each photo with an agent of mechanical weathering.

CCC Stability and Change How might more than one agent of mechanical weathering operate in the same place?

Investigate Look at how ice helps to break down rock.

Weathering Earth's Surface

The type of weathering in which rock is physically broken into smaller pieces is called **mechanical weathering**. A second type of weathering, called chemical weathering, also breaks down rock. **Chemical weathering** is the process that breaks down rock through chemical changes.

Mechanical Weathering Rocks that are cracked or split in layers have undergone mechanical weathering. Mechanical weathering usually happens gradually, over very long periods of time. Mechanical weathering, along with erosion, can eventually wear away whole mountains.

The natural agents of mechanical weathering include freezing and thawing, release of pressure, plant growth, actions of animals, and abrasion, as shown in **Figure 2**. Abrasion (uh BRAY zhun) refers to the wearing away of rock by rock particles carried by water, ice, wind, or gravity. Human activities, such as mining and farming, also cause mechanical weathering.

Through mechanical weathering, Earth systems interact and shape the surface. For example, the geosphere (rocks) interacts with the hydrosphere (water, ice) during frost wedging. Frost wedging occurs when water seeps into cracks in rocks and expands as it freezes. Wedges of ice in rocks widen and deepen cracks. When the ice melts, water seeps deeper into the cracks. With repeated freezing and thawing, the cracks slowly expand until pieces of rock break off.

Chemical Weathering Chemical weathering often produces new minerals as it breaks down rock. For example, granite is made up of several minerals, including feldspars. Chemical weathering occurs when feldspar is exposed to water. The material in the feldspar undergoes chemical changes that form clay minerals.

Water, oxygen, carbon dioxide, living organisms, and acid rain cause chemical weathering. Water weathers some rock by dissolving it. Water also carries other substances, including oxygen, carbon dioxide, and other chemicals, that dissolve or break down rock.

The oxygen and carbon dioxide gases in the atmosphere cause chemical weathering. Rust forms when iron combines with oxygen in the presence of water. Rusting makes rock soft and crumbly and gives it a red or brown color. When carbon dioxide dissolves in water, carbonic acid forms. This weak acid easily weathers certain types of rock, such as marble and limestone.

As a plant's roots grow, they produce weak acids that gradually dissolve rock. Lichens—plantlike organisms that grow on rocks—also produce weak acids.

Humans escalate chemical weathering by burning fossil fuels. This pollutes the air and results in rainwater that is more strongly acidic, shortening the time scale for weathering rock.

CHECK POINT **Summarize Text** How are the agents of weathering similar and different?

....

....

Literacy Connection

Write Explanatory Texts
An ancient marble statue is moved from a rural location to a highly polluted city. Explain how the move might affect the statue and why you think so.

....

....

....

....

....

....

....

Find out how weathering rates help with dating.

Rate of Weathering In historic cemeteries, slate tombstones from the 1700s are less weathered than marble tombstones from the 1800s. Why? Some kinds of rocks weather more rapidly than others. The rate at which weathering occurs is determined by the type of rock and the climate.

Type of Rock Rocks wear down slowly if they are made of minerals that do not dissolve easily. Rocks weather faster if they are made of minerals that dissolve easily.

Some rocks weather more easily because they are permeable. A permeable (PUR mee uh bul) material is full of tiny air spaces. The spaces increase the surface area. As water seeps through the spaces in the rock, it carries chemicals that dissolve the rock and removes material broken down by weathering.

Climate Climate is the average weather conditions in an area. Weathering occurs faster in wet climates. Rainfall causes chemical changes. Freezing and thawing cause mechanical changes in cold and wet climates.

Chemical reactions occur faster at higher temperatures. That is why chemical weathering occurs more quickly where the climate is both hot and wet. Human activities, such as those that produce acid rain, also increase the rate of weathering.

Comparing Weathered Limestone

The data table shows how much rock was broken down by weathering for two identical pieces of limestone in two different locations.

1. **Construct Graphs** Use the data to make a double-line graph. Decide how to make each line look different. Be sure to provide a title and label the axes and each graph line.
2. **SEP Use Mathematics** Compare the slopes of each line.

....

....

3. **Reason Quantitatively** As time increases, the limestone thickness (increases/decreases).
4. **SEP Analyze Data** Limestone A weathered at a (slower/faster) rate than Limestone B.

Weathering Rates of Limestone

Time (years)	Thickness of Limestone Lost (mm)	
	Limestone A	Limestone B
200	1.75	0.80
400	3.50	1.60
600	5.25	2.40
800	7.00	3.20
1,000	8.75	4.00

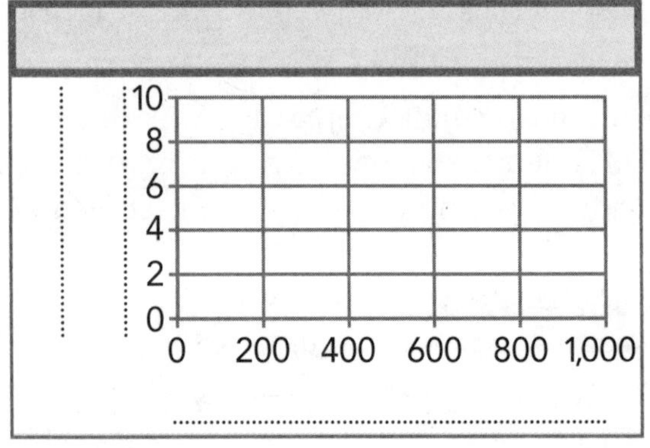

Forming Soil

Have you ever wondered how plants grow on rocks? Plants can grow only when soil begins to form in the cracks. **Soil** is the loose, weathered material on Earth's surface in which plants grow.

Soil Composition Soil is a mixture of rock particles, minerals, decayed organic material, water, and air. The main **components** of soil come from bedrock. Bedrock is the solid layer of rock beneath the soil. Once bedrock is exposed to air, water, and living things, it gradually weathers into smaller and smaller particles.

The particles of rock in soil are classified by size as gravel, sand, silt, and clay. **Figure 3** shows the relative sizes of these particles. A soil's texture depends on the size of the soil particles.

The decayed organic material in soil is called humus. **Humus** (HYOO mus) is a dark-colored substance that forms as plant and animal remains decay. Humus helps to create spaces in soil that are then filled by air and water. It contains nutrients that plants need.

CHECK POINT **Write Explanatory Texts** Explain how you might determine the rate of weathering on a sample of rock.

....

....

....

....

....

Soil Particle Size

Figure 3 The rock particles shown here have been enlarged. On the graph, mark the size of a 1.5-mm particle with an X.

Classify Explain how you would classify that size particle and why.

....

....

....

Academic Vocabulary

What are the similarities between components of a computer and the components of soil?

....

....

....

....

INTERACTIVITY

Learn how minerals affect the colors of sand.

INTERACTIVITY

Identify different types of weathering.

Soil Formation Soil forms in areas where rock is broken down by weathering and mixes with other materials on the surface. Soil forms constantly wherever bedrock weathers. Soil formation continues over a long period of time, taking hundreds to thousands of years. The same process that forms soil today was also taking place billions of years ago and will continue to form soil in the future.

Gradually, soil develops layers called horizons. A soil horizon is a layer of soil that differs in color, texture, and composition from the layers above or below it. **Figure 4** shows the sequence in which soil horizons form. In areas where weathering does not take place, soil is not as likely to form. This causes an uneven distribution of soil on Earth.

Soil and Organisms Recall that organisms are part of Earth's biosphere. Many organisms live in soil and interact with the geosphere. Some soil organisms aid in the formation of humus, which makes soil rich in the nutrients that plants need. Other soil organisms mix the soil and make spaces in it for air and water.

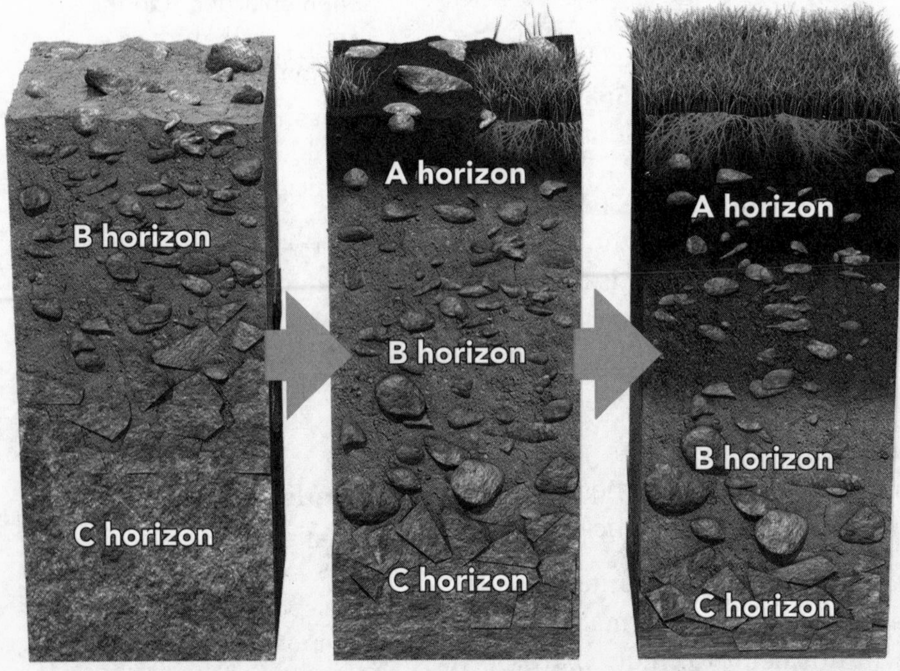

A horizon
The A horizon is made up of topsoil, a crumbly, dark brown soil that is a mixture of humus, clay, and minerals. Topsoil forms as plants add organic material to the soil, and plant roots weather pieces of rock.

B horizon
The B horizon, often called subsoil, usually consists of clay and other particles of rock, but little humus. It forms as rainwater washes these materials down from the A horizon.

C horizon
The C horizon forms as bedrock begins to weather. The rock breaks up into small particles.

Soil Horizons

Figure 4 Soil horizons form in three main steps.

1. **SEP Use Models** Underline the soil horizon that contains the most organic matter.
2. **SEP Construct Explanations** In what climates would you expect soil to form fastest? Why?

....

....

Forming Humus Dead leaves, roots, and other plant materials contribute most of the organic remains that form humus. Humus forms in a process called decomposition carried out by a combination of decomposers including fungi, bacteria, worms, and other organisms. Decomposers break down the remains of dead organisms into smaller pieces through the process of chemical digestion. This material then mixes with the soil as nutrient-rich humus where it can be used by living plants. Farmers can help humus form by introducing compost such as decaying leaves or even seaweed.

Mixing the Soil Earthworms and burrowing mammals mix humus with air and other materials in soil, as shown in **Figure 5**. As earthworms eat their way through the soil, they carry humus down to the subsoil and from the subsoil up to the surface. These organisms increase the soil's fertility by dispersing organic matter throughout the soil. Mammals such as mice, moles, and prairie dogs break up hard, compacted soil and mix humus with it. Animal wastes contribute nutrients to the soil as well. Farmers will often mix, or till, topsoil to improve its quality.

Organisms Impact Soil

Figure 5 Earthworms and chipmunks break up hard, compacted soil, making it easier for air and water to enter the soil.

1. **SEP Synthesize Information** Besides breaking up and mixing soil, the (earthworm/ chipmunk) is also a decomposer.
2. **CCC Systems** As these organisms change the soil, which Earth systems are interacting?

....

....

CHECK POINT **Integrate with Visuals** Review the information and illustrations in **Figure 4**. How is weathering related to soil formation?

....

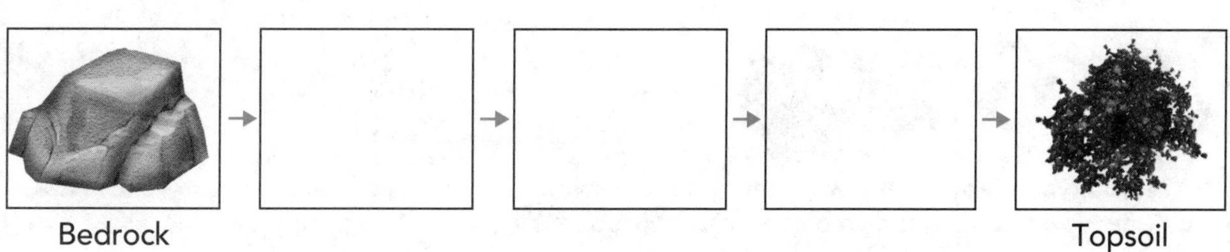

From Rock to Soil

Figure 6 The illustrations show bedrock and topsoil rich in humus.

1. **SEP Develop Models** In the empty boxes, draw the processes that help to change the bedrock into soil. Label the processes in each drawing. Include at least two processes that involve organisms.
2. **SEP Use Models** The topsoil represents the (A/B/C) horizon.

LESSON 1 Check

MS-ESS2-2, EP&CIc

1. CCC Cause and Effect How does erosion affect Earth's surface?

Erosion affects the earth's surface by bycicles to rust, paint peeling, and sidewalks to crack.

2. SEP Construct Explanations Explain how water can wear down Earth's surface at scales that are large and small in size, or short and long in duration.

Water, can dissolves the rocks oxygen, CO_2, and other chemicals can break down rocks.

3. Compare and Contrast Compare and contrast mechanical weathering and chemical weathering.

Mechanical weathering physically breaks rocks but chemical weather breaks down rocks chemically.

4. SEP Evaluate Information A community group needs advice on choosing rock for a city park monument that will last a long time. Explain the factors that would likely affect how long the monument lasts.

The monument should made out of clay because clay has the least amount of air spaces which then water can't get through.

5. CCC Stability and Change How did organisms change the soil in North America over millions of years? Cite evidence to support your answer.

Chipmanks break up hard soil so then water can go into the soil easier.

Quest CHECK-IN

In this lesson, you learned how weathering and erosion change Earth's surface. You also discovered how soil forms.

SEP Use Models How can modeling the effects of weathering on different materials help you to design your island?

HANDS-ON LAB

Breaking It Down

Go online to download the lab worksheet. Investigate what constraints need to be considered when designing an island to resist long-term erosion.

uEngineer It! Defining the Problem STEM

littleBits

MS-ESS2-2, MS-ESS3-2, EP&CIc

GROUND SHIFTING ADVANCES: Maps Help Predict

INTERACTIVITY

Learn about the causes of landslides and predict where they might occur.

Do you know what happens after heavy rains or earthquakes in California? There are landslides. Engineers look for patterns to determine how and where they can happen.

The Challenge: To protect highways and towns from landslides.

Landslides destroy roadways, cut people off from access to vital services, and disrupt local economies.

Phenomenon Evaluating hazards is one way to prepare for natural disasters. In the early 1970s, the California Geological Survey (CGS) began drawing up "Geology for Planning" maps. Its goal was to create maps showing areas all over the state where natural hazards, such as wildfires and landslides, were most likely to occur. Engineers and city planners could then use the maps to prepare for, or possibly prevent, natural disasters.

In 1997, the Caltrans Highway Corridor Mapping project began. Caltrans stands for California Department of Transportation. Caltrans engineers set out to map all known sites of landslides, as well as unstable slopes along the major interstate highways. Most of the landslide sites were along highways that wind through California's mountains. Using these maps, engineers have installed sensitive monitoring equipment to help predict future landslides.

DESIGN CHALLENGE
Can you design a solution to protect a roadway from a landslide? Go to the Engineering Design Notebook to find out!

LESSON

2 Erosion and Deposition

HANDS-ON LAB

uInvestigate Examine how particle size affects erosion and deposition.

MS-ESS2-2 Construct an explanation based on evidence for how geoscience processes have changed Earth's surface at varying time and spatial scales.

MS-ESS3-2 Analyze and interpret data on natural hazards to forecast future catastrophic events and inform the development of technologies to mitigate their effects.

Connect It!

Circle the change shown in the photo, then draw an arrow to show the direction of the rocks' movement.

CCC Stability and Change How has Earth's surface changed in this photo?

CCC Cause and Effect What natural processes do you think caused the change you observe?

Changing Earth's Surface

Have you ever watched water carry away bits of gravel and soil during a rainstorm? If so, you observed erosion. Recall that erosion is a process that moves weathered rock from its original location. Gravity, water, ice, and wind are all agents of erosion that allow for materials to be transported.

The process of erosion moves material called **sediment**. Sediment may consist of pieces of rock or soil, or the remains of plants and animals.

Deposition occurs where the agents of erosion deposit, or lay down, sediment. Like erosion, deposition changes the shape of Earth's surface. You may have watched an ant carry away bits of soil and then put the soil down in a different location to build an ant hill. The ant's activity is **similar** to erosion and deposition, which involves picking up, carrying away, and putting down sediment in a different place.

Weathering, erosion, transportation, and deposition act together in a continuous cycle that wears down and builds up Earth's surface. As erosion wears down a mountain in one place, deposition builds up a new landform in another place. Some changes happen over a large area, while others occur in a small space. Some occur over a timescale of thousands or millions of years, and others take only a few moments, such as the rockslide shown in **Figure 1**. No matter how large or fast the changes, the cycle of erosion and deposition is continuous. The same changes that shaped Earth's surface in the past still shape it today and will continue to shape it in the future.

Academic Vocabulary

Using two things you can observe right now, write a sentence describing how they are similar.

....

....

....

....

Literacy Connection

Integrate with Visuals

In the third paragraph of the text, underline a statement that is supported by evidence in the photograph.

Moving Rock

Figure 1 The sudden change in the appearance of this hillside along one of the Cottonwood lakes near Lone Pine, California, was was caused by the natural movement of rock.

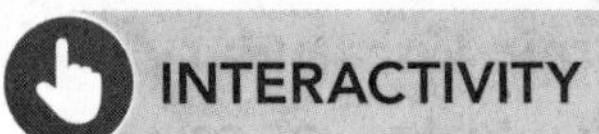

INTERACTIVITY

Explore the ways slope influences mass movement.

Mass Movement

If you place a ball at the top of a hill, with a slight push the ball will roll down the hill. Gravity pulls the ball downward. Gravity is also the force that moves rock and other materials downhill.

Gravity causes **mass movement**, one of several processes that move sediment downhill. Mass movement can be rapid or slow. Erosion and deposition both take place during a mass movement event. The different types of mass movement include landslides, mudflows, slumps, and creep (**Figure 2**).

A mass movement may be caused by a natural disaster, such as a flood, earthquake, or hurricane. Natural disasters can dramatically and suddenly change Earth's surface. Scientists use satellites to monitor mass movement and make maps of past mass movements in a region to better understand their hazards. Such maps help scientists to identify patterns and predict where future mass movement is likely to occur in order to prevent human casualties. To help reduce the effects of mass movement, engineers may implement different technologies. Retaining walls, wire mesh, drainage pipes, and increased vegetation can help stabilize a slope.

CHECK POINT **Integrate with Visuals** Read and think about the information relating to different kinds of mass movement. Which type of mass movement do you think is least dangerous? Why?

....

Mass Movement

Figure 2 Different types of mass movement have different characteristics.

1. SEP Develop Models Draw arrows on each image of mass movement to show the direction that material moves.
2. CCC Patterns What pattern(s) can you identify among the types of mass movement?

....

....

Landslides

A landslide occurs when rock and soil slide quickly down a steep slope. Some landslides contain huge masses of rock, while others contain only small amounts of rock and soil. Often caused by earthquakes, landslides occur where road builders have cut highways through hills or mountains, leaving behind unstable slopes.

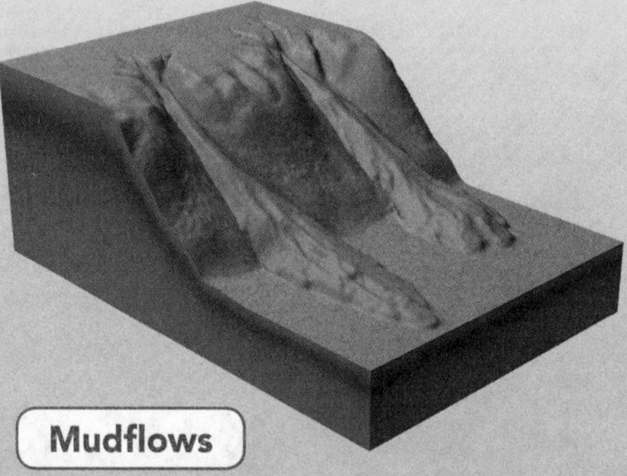

Mudflows

A mudflow is the rapid downhill movement of a mixture of water, rock, and soil. Mudflows often occur after heavy rains in a normally dry area. In clay-rich soils with a high water content, mudflows may occur even on very gentle slopes. Under certain conditions, clay-rich soil suddenly behaves as a liquid and begins to flow.

Major Landslides and Mudflows

Landslides and mudflows are a problem in all 50 states and all around the world. Annually in the United States, landslides cause $1 billion to $2 billion in damage and about 25 deaths. But some catastrophic mass movements in other countries have killed more than 100,000 people.

1. **CCC Scale, Proportion, and Quantity** What proportion of the landslides were caused by earthquakes?

2. **Analyze Quantitative Relationships** Which process caused the most landslides? Which caused the fewest landslides?

Major Landslides and Mudflows

Year	Location	Cause
1919	Java, Indonesia	volcanic eruption
1920	Ningxia, China	earthquake
1933	Sichuan, China	earthquake
1949	Tadzhikistan	earthquake
1958	Japan	heavy rains
1970	Peru	earthquake
1980	Washington, USA	earthquakes
1983	Utah, USA	heavy rain and snowmelt
1985	Colombia	volcano
1998	Central America	hurricane rains
2017	California, USA	heavy rains

Slumps

In a slump, a mass of rock and soil suddenly slips down a slope. Unlike a landslide, the material in a slump moves down in one large mass. It looks as if someone pulled the bottom out from under part of the slope. A slump often occurs when water soaks the bottom of clay-rich soil.

Creep

Creep is the very slow downhill movement of rock and soil. It can even occur on gentle slopes. Creep often results from the freezing and thawing of water in cracked layers of rock beneath the soil. Even though it occurs slowly, you can see the effects of creep in vertical objects such as telephone poles and tree trunks. Creep may tilt these objects at unusual angles.

Investigate Examine how particle size affects erosion and deposition.

Academic Vocabulary

Describe a significant change in weather from the winter to the summer.

....

....

....

Erosion and Deposition by Wind

Recall that wind, or moving air, is an agent of erosion and deposition. Through these processes, wind wears down and builds up Earth's surface.

Wind Erosion Wind can be a **significant** agent in shaping the land in areas where there are few plants to hold the soil in place. In a sandstorm, strong winds pick up large amounts of sediment and loose soil and transport it to new locations.

Deflation Wind causes erosion mainly by **deflation**, the process by which wind removes surface materials. You can see the process of deflation in **Figure 3**. When wind blows over the land, it picks up the smallest particles of sediment, such as clay and silt. Stronger, faster winds pick up larger particles. Slightly larger particles, such as sand, might skip or bounce for a short distance. Strong winds can roll even larger and heavier sediment particles. In deserts, deflation can create an area called desert pavement where smaller sediments are blown away, and larger rock fragments are left behind.

Abrasion Wind, water, and ice carry particles that rub or scrape against exposed rock. As particles move against the rock, friction wears away the rock by the process of abrasion, a type of mechanical weathering.

Wind Erosion and Deflation

Figure 3 Wind causes deflation by moving surface particles in three ways.

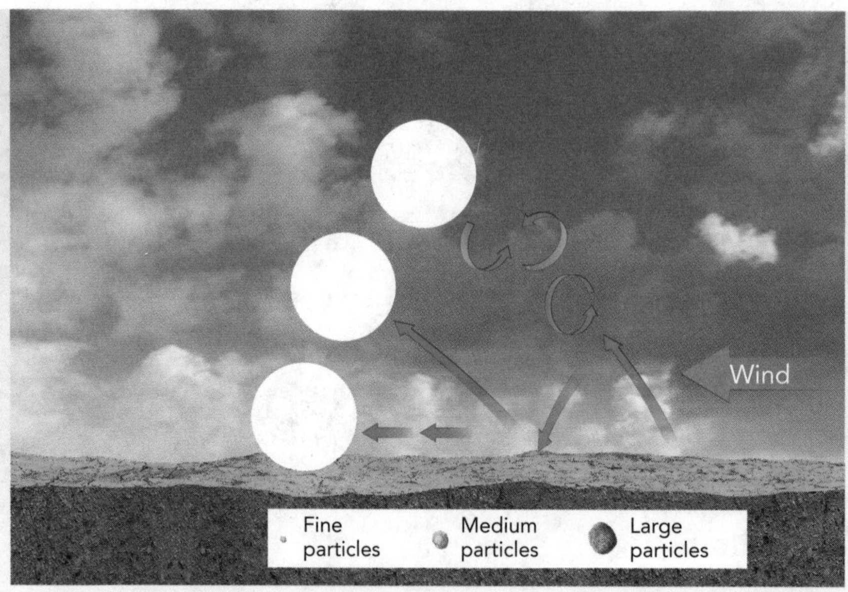

1. Claim In each circle, draw the size of particles that would be moved by the wind.
2. Evidence How does a particle's size affect how high and far it travels?

....

....

....

3. Reasoning Complete each sentence to the right with one of the following words: Fine, Medium, Large.

.... particles are carried through the air.

.... particles skip or bounce.

.... particles slide or roll.

Wind Deposition All the sediment picked up by wind eventually falls back to Earth's surface. This happens when the wind slows down or encounters an obstacle. Wind deposition may form sand dunes and loess deposits.

Sand Dunes When wind meets an obstacle, such as a clump of grass, it can produce a deposit of windblown sand called a **sand dune**. **Figure 4** shows how wind direction can form different dunes. The shape and size of sand dunes is determined by the direction of the wind, the amount of sand, and the presence of plants. This same process changed Earth's surface billions of years ago, just as it does today. You can predict how wind deposition will affect the surface in the future. You can see sand dunes on beaches and in deserts where wind-blown sediment builds up. Sand dunes also move over time because the sand shifts with the wind from one side of the dune to the other. Sometimes plants begin growing on a dune, and the roots help to anchor the dune in one place.

Loess Deposits The wind drops sediment that is finer than sand but coarser than clay far from its source. This fine, wind-deposited sediment is **loess** (LOH es). There are large loess deposits in central China and in states such as Nebraska, South Dakota, Iowa, Missouri, and Illinois. Loess helps to form soil rich in nutrients. Many areas with thick loess deposits are valuable farmlands.

CHECK POINT **Cite Textual Evidence** What factors affect wind erosion and deposition?

Moving Sand Dunes

Sand dunes keep drifting and covering a nearby, busy parking lot.

SEP Define Problems State the problem that needs to be solved in the form of a question.

SEP Design Solutions Describe two possible solutions to the problem. Explain why each would solve the problem.

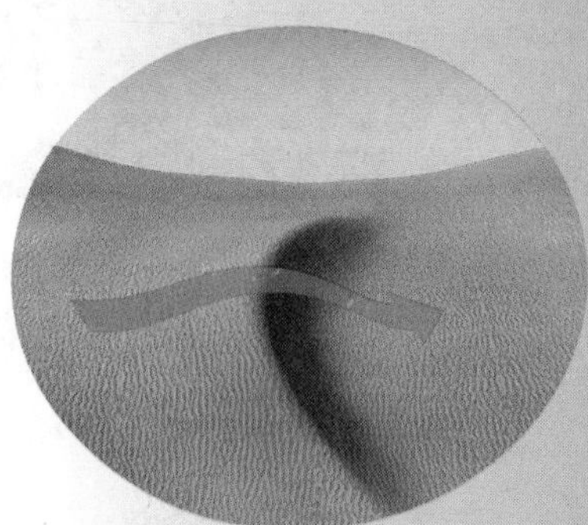

Crescent-shaped dune

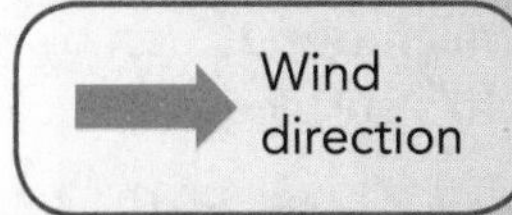

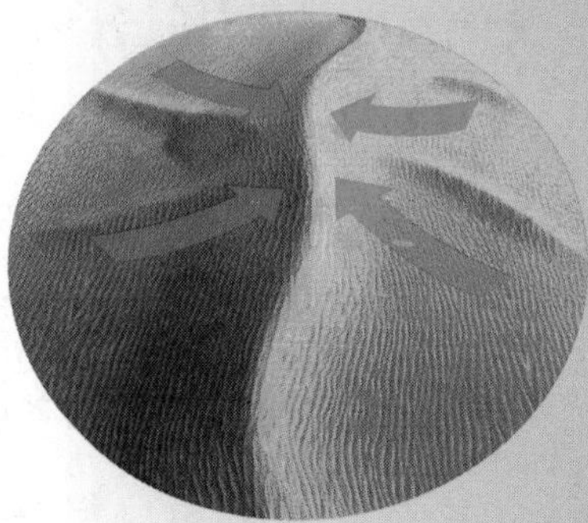

Star-shaped dunes

Dune Formation

Figure 4 Sand dunes form and change shape as the wind deposits sand.

1. Predict Draw a line to show how the ridge of the crescent-shaped dune will likely shift over time.
2. CCC Cause and Effect Why do these dunes have different shapes?

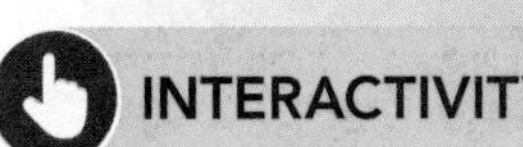

Explore fast and slow changes to Earth's surface.

LESSON 2 Check

MS-ESS2-2, MS-ESS3-2

1. **Classify** Which kinds of mass movement happen quickly?

   Landslides, Mud flows, and Slumps

2. **CCC Stability and Change** Describe a way in which deposition by gravity slowly changes Earth's surface.

   Landslides can slowely change Earth's surface by deposition. New destroyed habitats, land forms, and clog.

3. **CCC Patterns** Explain how the wind both builds up and wears down Earth's surface in a desert. Give examples of features that result from these processes.

   Fast winds can pick up sand which can make sanddunes.

4. **SEP Construct Explanations** Explain why a scientist may organize evidence of landslides in a certain area by drawing a scale map.

5. **SEP Interpret Data** Two towns are located in the same dry region. Town X has steeper slopes than Town Y. Town Y gets heavier than normal rain for several days while Town X remains dry. Which town is more likely to experience mass movement in the near future? Explain your answer.

Quest CHECK-INS

In this lesson, you learned how gravity is involved in erosion and deposition. You also learned how wind causes erosion and deposition.

CCC System Models What are some ways that the effects of erosion can be mitigated in your design for the artificial island?

HANDS-ON LAB

Ingenious Island, Part I

INTERACTIVITY

Changing Landscapes

Go online to download the lab worksheet. Test your island's resistance to erosion by surface water.

Go online to explore how landscapes can be changed.

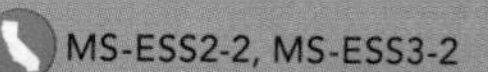

MS-ESS2-2, MS-ESS3-2

CAREERS

Civil Engineer

Civil Engineers SAVE THE DAY!

Who put the civil in civilization? Engineers! Civil engineers are responsible for all the works that benefit the citizens of a society. After a natural disaster, civil engineers get involved in reconstruction efforts.

Think of the networks and systems Californians rely on every day—roadways, train tracks, cell phone towers, gas and electrical lines. Consider the Los Angeles aqueduct system that carries water for about 675 km (419 mi). Think of the Golden Gate Bridge that links San Francisco and Marin County. Civil engineers and the construction workers they guided made all of this possible.

Whether planning a new road or bridge, civil engineers must take into account the forces that change Earth's surface. Water and wind erosion, for example, have serious effects on roadways and can cause costly damage. A civil engineer's job is to determine how to build the road in a way that minimizes, or mitigates, nature's potentially damaging effects.

If you want to be a civil engineer, you'll need to study science and math. You'll also need to develop your imagination, because solutions require creativity as well as analytical thinking.

VIDEO

Watch what's involved in being a civil engineer.

DOCUMENT

Go online to explore more science and engineering careers.

MY CAREER

Type "civil engineer" into an online search engine to learn more about this career.

Civil engineers retrofit the San Mateo-Hayward Bridge in California to help withstand damage from earthquakes.

LESSON

3 Water Erosion

HANDS-ON LAB

uInvestigate Trace the paths raindrops can follow after hitting the ground.

MS-ESS2-2 Construct an explanation based on evidence for how geoscience processes have changed Earth's surface at varying time and spatial scales.

Connect It!

Circle an area on the image that shows where water has changed the rock on these cliffs.

CCC Stability and Change Describe how the water waves shape the surface of the cliffs.

How Water Causes Erosion

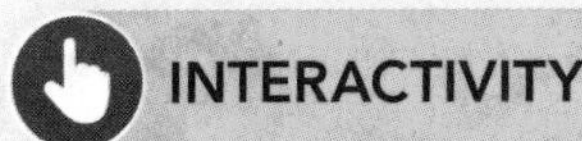

INTERACTIVITY

Locate evidence of water erosion and determine why it happened.

Erosion by water begins with a little splash of rain. Some rainfall sinks into the ground, where it is absorbed by plant roots. Some water evaporates, while the rest of the water runs off over the land surface. Moving water of the hydrosphere is the primary agent of the erosion that shaped Earth's land surface, the geosphere, for billions of years. It continues to shape the surface today in small and large ways. **Figure 1** shows how moving water can shape a landscape over time through erosion.

Literacy Connection

Cite Textual Evidence As you read the second paragraph, number the factors that affect runoff.

Runoff As water moves over the land, it picks up and carries sediment. This moving water is called **runoff**. When runoff flows over the land, it may cause a type of erosion called sheet erosion, where thin layers of soil are removed. The amount of runoff in an area depends on five main factors. The first factor is the amount of rain an area gets. A heavy or lengthy rainfall can add water to the surface more quickly than the surface can absorb it. A second factor is vegetation. Grasses, shrubs, and trees reduce runoff by absorbing water and holding soil in place. A third factor is the type of soil. Different types of soils absorb different amounts of water. A fourth factor is the shape of the land. Runoff is more likely to occur on steeply sloped land than on flatter land. Finally, a fifth factor is how people use land. For example, pavement does not absorb water. All the rain that falls on it becomes runoff. Runoff also increases when trees or crops are cut down, because this removes vegetation from the land.

Factors that reduce runoff also reduce erosion. Even though deserts have little rainfall, they often have high runoff and erosion because they have few plants and thin, sandy soil. In wet areas, such as rain forests and wetlands, runoff and erosion may be low because there are more plants to protect the soil.

Sunset Cliffs

Figure 1 Waves crashing against the rocks of Sunset Cliffs in Point Loma, California, change the shape of the land.

Stream Formation Gravity causes runoff and the sediment it carries to flow downhill. As runoff moves across the land, it flows together to form rills, gullies, and streams, as shown in **Figure 2**.

HANDS-ON LAB

Investigate Trace the paths raindrops can follow after hitting the ground.

Rills and Gullies As runoff travels, it forms tiny grooves in the soil called rills. Many rills flow into one another to form a gully. A gully is a large groove, or channel, in the soil that carries runoff after a rainstorm. As water flows through gullies, it picks up and moves sediment with it, thus enlarging the gullies through erosion.

Streams and Rivers Gullies join to form a stream. A **stream** is a channel along which water is continually flowing down a slope. Unlike gullies, streams rarely dry up. Small streams are also known as creeks or brooks. As streams flow together, they form larger bodies of flowing water called rivers.

Tributaries A **tributary** is a stream or river that flows into a larger river. For example, the Missouri and Ohio rivers are tributaries of the Mississippi River. A drainage basin, or watershed, is the area from which a river and its tributaries collect their water.

CHECK POINT **Integrate with Visuals** Review the information in paragraph 2 and in **Figure 2**. How does the amount of water change as it moves from rills and gullies to streams?

....

....

Stream Formation

Figure 2 In the diagram, shade only the arrows that indicate the direction of runoff flow that causes erosion.

CCC Cause and Effect How will the depth of the channel likely change with further erosion?

....

....

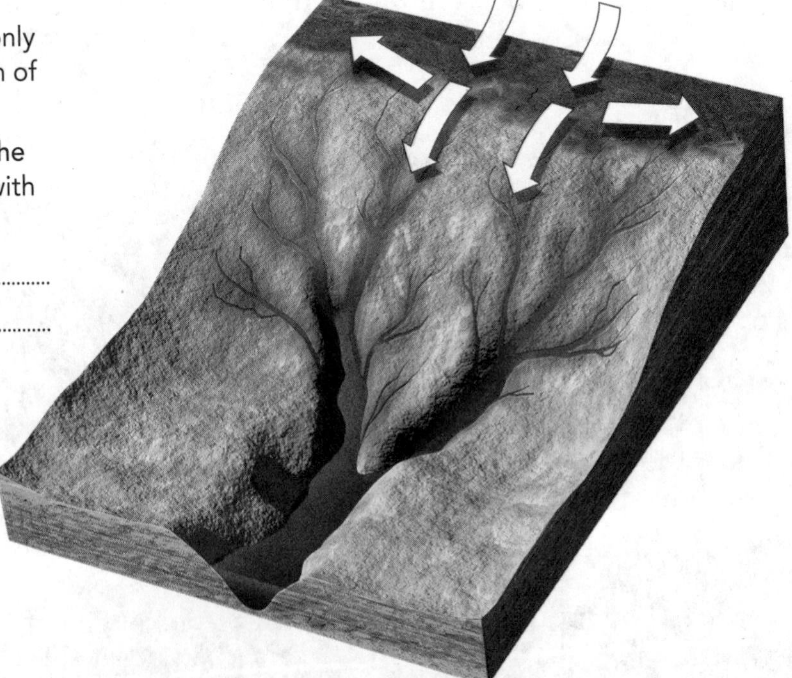

Waterfalls

Figure 3 Waterfalls form where rivers erode hard and soft rock layers at different rates.

1. **SEP Use Models** The rock at the top of the waterfall erodes at a (slower/faster) rate than the rock below it.
2. **Predict** How do you think erosion will change this waterfall in the next 100 years?

Water Erosion and Deposition Change Earth's Surface

Some landforms result from erosion by rivers and streams, while others result from deposition. Still other landforms are created from a combination of these processes. Erosion by water removes particles on Earth's surface, while deposition by water builds it up.

Water Erosion Many rivers begin on steep mountain slopes as flowing rain water or melted snow. This running water starts out fast-flowing and generally follows a straight, narrow course. The steep slopes along the river erode rapidly, resulting in a deep, V-shaped valley. As a river flows to the sea, it forms other features such as waterfalls, flood plains, meanders, and oxbow lakes.

Waterfalls Waterfalls, as shown in **Figure 3,** may occur where a river meets an area of hard, slowly eroding rock. The river flows over this rock and erodes softer rock downstream. Eventually a waterfall develops where the softer rock has worn away. Rushing water and sediment can cause further erosion at the base of the waterfall. Rough water rapids also occur where a river tumbles over hard rock, wearing away the supporting rock base and leaving the rock above it unsupported.

Flood Plains Lower down on its course, a river usually flows over more gently sloping land. The river spreads out and erodes the land along its side, forming a wide river valley. The flat, wide area of land along a river is a **flood plain**. During a flood or a rainy season, a river overflows its banks and flows onto the flood plain. As the flood water retreats, it deposits sediment. This gradually makes the soil of a flood plain rich in nutrients.

Academic Vocabulary

What things did you develop in science class this year? Name two examples.

....

....

....

VIDEO

Explore landforms caused by water erosion.

Meanders A river often **develops** meanders where it flows through easily eroded rock or sediment. A meander is a loop-like bend in the course of a river. A meandering river erodes sediment from the outer bank and deposits the sediment on the inner bank farther downstream. The water flows faster in the deeper, outer section of each bend, causing more erosion. Over time, a meander becomes more curved.

Flood plains also follow the meander as sediment erodes more of the land to the side of the river. Here, the river's channel is often deep and wide. For example, the southern stretch of the Mississippi River meanders on a wide, gently sloping flood plain.

Oxbow Lakes Sometimes a meandering river forms a feature called an oxbow lake. An oxbow lake occurs when a meander develops such a large loop that the bends of the river join together. Sediment deposits block the ends of the bends, cutting off the river flow. Oxbow lakes are the remains of the river's former bend, seen in **Figure 4**.

CHECK POINT **Cite Textual Evidence** What evidence supports the idea that a flood plain is formed by erosion and deposition?

....

....

....

Model It!

Oxbow Lakes

Figure 4 A meander may gradually form an oxbow lake.

SEP Develop Models Draw steps 2 and 4 to show how an oxbow lake forms. Then describe step 4.

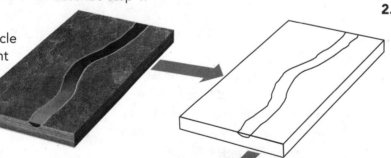

1. A small obstacle creates a slight bend in the river.

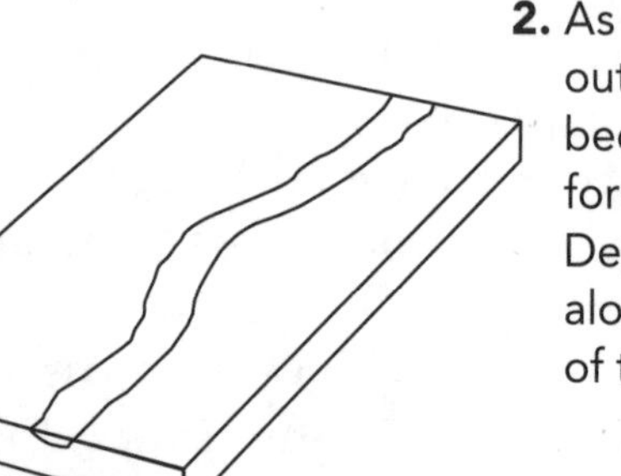

2. As water erodes the outer edge, the bend becomes bigger, forming a meander. Deposition occurs along the inside bend of the river.

3. Gradually, the meander becomes more curved. The river breaks through and takes a new course.

4. ....

Delta and Alluvial Fan

Figure 5 ✏ Draw arrows to show the direction in which water carries sediment to each landform.

Interpret Photos Record your observations about deltas and alluvial fans.

....

....

....

....

....

....

....

Water Deposition Any time moving water slows, it deposits some of the sediment it carries. First, larger rocks stop rolling and sliding as fast-moving water starts to slow down. Then, finer and finer particles fall to the river's bed as the water flows even more slowly. In this way, water deposition builds up Earth's surface and produces landforms such as deltas and alluvial fans.

Deltas Eventually, a river flows into a body of water, such as an ocean or a lake. Because the river water no longer flows downhill, the water slows down. At this point, the sediment in the water drops to the bottom. Sediment deposited where a river flows into an ocean or lake builds up a landform called a **delta**. Some deltas are arc-shaped, while others are triangular. The delta of the Mississippi River, shown in **Figure 5**, is an example of a type of delta called a "bird's foot" delta.

Alluvial Fans When a stream flows out of a steep, narrow mountain valley, it suddenly becomes wider and shallower. The water slows down and deposits sediments in an **alluvial fan**. An alluvial fan is a wide, sloping deposit of sediment formed where a stream leaves a mountain range. As its name **suggests**, this deposit is shaped like a fan.

Academic Vocabulary

Suggest means "to mention as a possibility." Use *suggest* in a sentence.

....

....

....

....

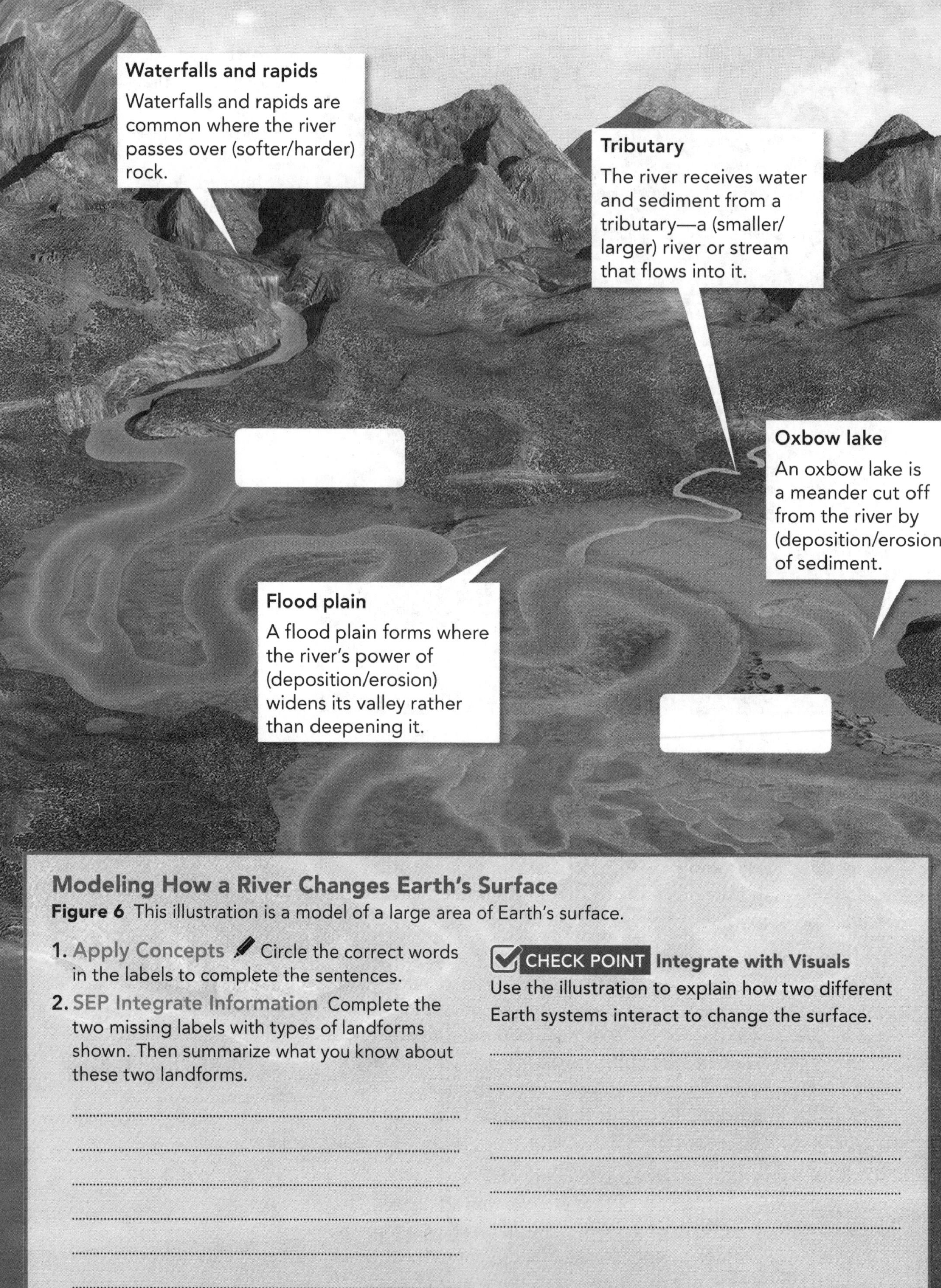

Waterfalls and rapids
Waterfalls and rapids are common where the river passes over (softer/harder) rock.
Tributary
The river receives water and sediment from a tributary—a (smaller/larger) river or stream that flows into it.
Oxbow lake
An oxbow lake is a meander cut off from the river by (deposition/erosion) of sediment.
Flood plain
A flood plain forms where the river's power of (deposition/erosion) widens its valley rather than deepening it.

Modeling How a River Changes Earth's Surface

Figure 6 This illustration is a model of a large area of Earth's surface.

1. Apply Concepts Circle the correct words in the labels to complete the sentences.
2. SEP Integrate Information Complete the two missing labels with types of landforms shown. Then summarize what you know about these two landforms.

CHECK POINT **Integrate with Visuals**
Use the illustration to explain how two different Earth systems interact to change the surface.

Groundwater Changes Earth's Surface

When rain falls and snow melts, some water soaks into the ground. It trickles into cracks and spaces in layers of soil and rock. **Groundwater** is the term geologists use for this underground water. Like moving water, groundwater changes the shape of Earth's surface.

Groundwater Erosion Groundwater causes erosion by chemical weathering. In the atmosphere, rain water combines with carbon dioxide to form a weak acid called carbonic acid, which can break down limestone. The water may also become more acidic as it flows through leaf debris before it seeps into the ground. When groundwater flows into cracks in limestone, some of the limestone dissolves and gets carried away. This process gradually hollows out pockets in the rock. Over time, large underground holes, called caves or caverns, develop.

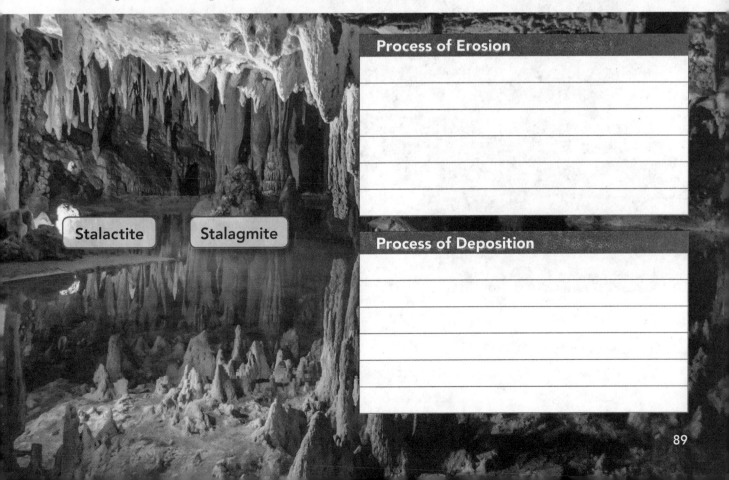

Groundwater Deposition The action of carbonic acid on limestone can also result in deposition. Water containing carbonic acid and calcium drips from a cave's roof. Carbon dioxide escapes from the solution, leaving behind a deposit of calcite. A deposit that hangs like an icicle from the roof of a cave is known as a stalactite (stuh LAK tyt). On the floor of the cave, a cone-shaped stalagmite (stuh LAG myt) builds up as water drops from the cave roof (**Figure 7**).

Write About It
Conduct research on the formation of California Cavern, a limestone cave in the Sierra Nevada foothills. In your science notebook, write a tourist brochure explaining how the cavern formed.

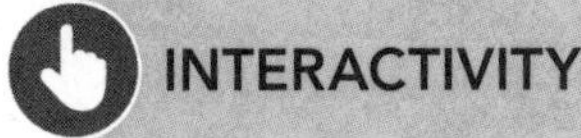

Explore erosion caused by groundwater.

Groundwater Erosion and Deposition

Figure 7 On the photo, draw a line from each label to the formation it names.

SEP Construct Explanations How do deposition and erosion shape caves? Outline your ideas in the table.

Stalactite

Stalagmite

Process of Erosion

Process of Deposition

INTERACTIVITY

Explore the impact of water on Earth's surface.

Karst Topography In rainy regions such as Florida where there is a layer of limestone near the surface, groundwater erosion can significantly change the shape of Earth's surface. Deep valleys and caverns commonly form. If the roof of a cave collapses because of limestone erosion, the result is a depression called a sinkhole. This type of landscape is called karst topography.

The formation of karst topography happens over small to large areas and over short to very long time periods. Groundwater erosion starts with a microscopic geochemical process: a single drop of water that dissolves a tiny amount of limestone in seconds. After 100 years, groundwater might deposit 1 or 2 cm of calcite on the roof of a cave. Erosion might take thousands to millions of years to form a deep valley or huge cave system hundreds of kilometers long. The roof of a cave may very slowly erode over hundreds of years, but collapse within minutes to form a small or large sinkhole, as shown in **Figure 8**.

CHECK POINT **Summarize** How does groundwater cause karst topography?

Karst Topography

Figure 8 This sinkhole formed in a day in Winter Park, Florida, in 1981. What was the cause of the sinkhole?

1. **SEP Use Models** Circle the state that has the most karst topography.
2. **Identify** Identify two states that have very little karst topography.

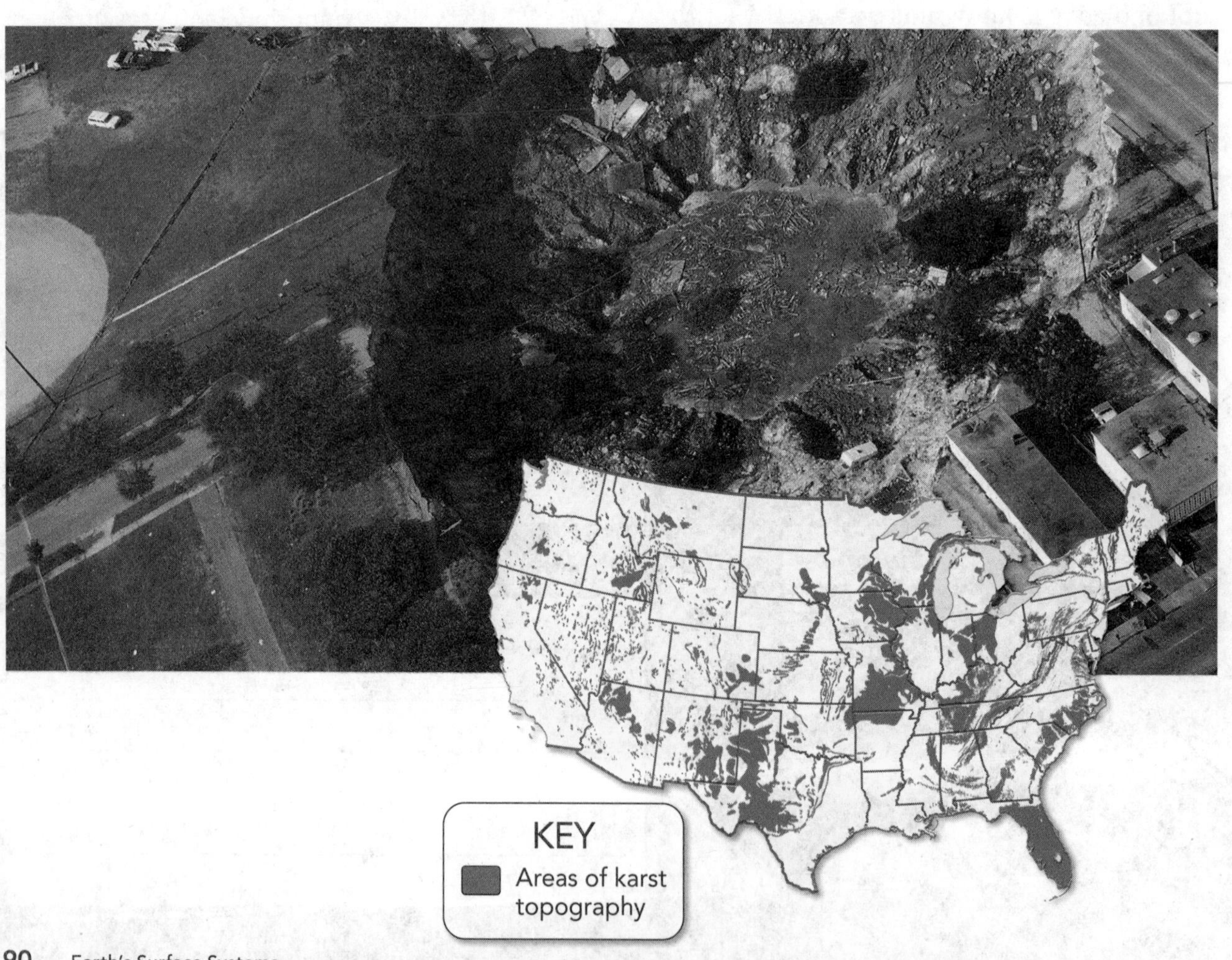

LESSON 3 Check

MS-ESS2-2

1. **Identify** What are two features that result from deposition by groundwater?

~~The action of carbonated acid on limestone.~~ Stalagmite or Stalactite

2. **CCC Cause and Effect** How does a meander form by erosion and deposition?

The meander river uses erosion from outer layer sediments and then deposits the sediments from inner layer

3. **CCC Stability and Change** Explain how water wearing down Earth's surface can produce a landform.

This is water can creat a landform. The water slowly erodes ~~[illegible]~~ then breaks down the moutain

4. **CCC Patterns** How will Niagara Falls most likely change naturally in the future?

Since the rock is constantly ~~moving~~ being eroded the Niagra Falls will most likely change.

5. **SEP Evaluate Information** How does the following literary passage capture the time scale in which water erosion forms cave structures?

In one place, near at hand, a stalagmite had been slowly growing up from the ground for ages, builded by the waterdrip from a stalactite overhead.
— *The Adventures of Tom Sawyer*, Mark Twain

~~[illegible]~~ It takes a long time because the passage said that the stalagmite slowly forms from the ground for ages.

Quest CHECK-IN

In this lesson, you learned how water on Earth's surface causes erosion and deposition. You also found out how groundwater causes erosion and deposition.

SEP Evaluate Your Solution Why is it important to take different types of erosion and deposition into account when designing an artificial island?

HANDS-ON LAB

Ingenious Island: Part II

Go online to download the lab worksheet. Investigate how you can use a model to test the effects of the agents of erosion on your artificial island.

LESSON 4

Glacial and Wave Erosion

HANDS-ON LAB

uInvestigate Explore coastline erosion.

MS-ESS2-2 Construct an explanation based on evidence for how geoscience processes have changed Earth's surface at varying time and spatial scales. (Also **EP&CIc**)

Connect It!

Look closely at the image of the glacier. Draw an arrow showing the direction in which the glacier is flowing.

CCC Stability and Change How do you think this giant mass of ice changes Earth's surface?

....

....

Glaciers Change Earth's Surface

If you were to fly over Alaska, you would see snowcapped mountains and evergreen forests. Between the mountains and the Gulf of Alaska, you would also see a thick, winding mass of ice. This river of ice in **Figure 1** is a glacier. Geologists define a **glacier** (GLAY shur) as any large mass of ice that moves slowly over land. Typically, the effects of glaciers are measured on scales that are great in both distance and time.

Glaciers occur in the coldest places on Earth. That's because they can form only in an area where more snow falls than melts. Layers of snow pile on top of more layers of snow. Over time, the weight of the layers presses the particles of snow so tightly together that they form a solid block of ice.

Glaciers are part of the cryosphere (KRI oh sfear), the portion of the hydrosphere that includes all the frozen water on Earth. As glaciers move slowly over land, the cryosphere interacts with Earth's crust. This **interaction** changes Earth's surface through weathering, erosion, and deposition.

HANDS-ON LAB

Examine how glaciers move across Earth's surface.

Academic Vocabulary

Describe an interaction you observed and one you took part in. Be sure to identify the people and things involved in the interaction.

....

....

....

....

....

Giant Bulldozer of Ice

Figure 1 Like a slow-moving bulldozer, Alaska's Bering Glacier, the largest glacier in North America, plows across Earth's surface.

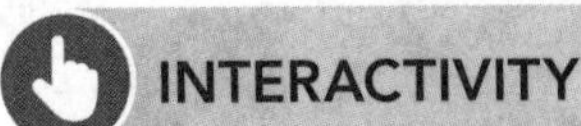

Learn about the effects of glaciers.

Continental Glaciers A **continental glacier** is a glacier that covers much of a continent or large island. It can spread out over millions of square kilometers and flow in all directions. Today, continental glaciers cover about 10 percent of Earth's land, including Antarctica and most of Greenland.

During **ice ages**, continental glaciers covered larger areas of Earth's surface. The glaciers gradually advanced and retreated several times, changing the shape of Earth's surface each time.

Valley Glaciers A **valley glacier** is a long, narrow glacier that forms when snow and ice build up in a mountain valley. High mountains keep these glaciers from spreading out in all directions, and gravity pulls the glacier downhill. Valley glaciers usually move slowly down valleys that have already been cut by rivers. Sometimes a valley glacier can experience a surge, or a quick slide, and move about 6 kilometers in one year. Alaska's Bering Glacier, shown in **Figure 1**, is a valley glacier.

Math Toolbox

Comparing Glacier Thickness

The graph shows the cumulative mass balance of a set of glaciers observed by scientists from 1945 to 2015. The cumulative mass balance is the total amount of ice the glaciers have gained or lost since 1945. The curve is negative, so the glaciers have lost ice since 1945. The slope of the curve (how steep it is) shows how quickly or slowly the glaciers have lost ice.

1. **Reason Abstractly** What does a flat slope indicate? What does a steep slope indicate?

2. **SEP Use Models** According to the data, the reference glaciers have melted and lost ice in every decade. In which decade did the glaciers lose ice slowest? In which decade did they lose ice quickest?

Average Cumulative Mass Balance of "Reference" Glaciers Worldwide, 1945–2015

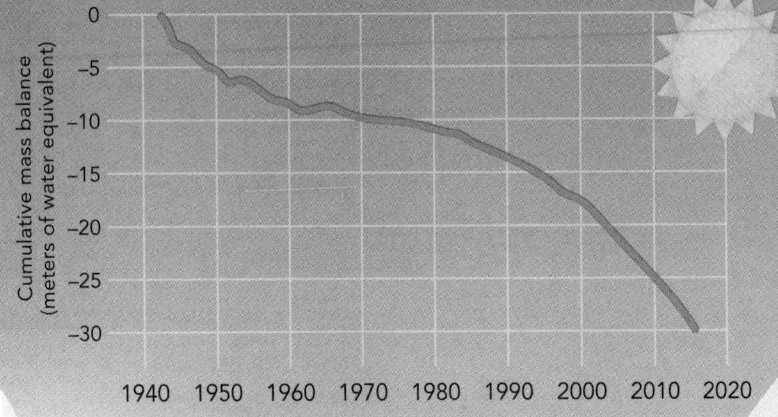

Source: World Glacier Monitoring Service, 2016

Glacial Erosion

Figure 2 Glaciers wear down Earth's surface by plucking and abrasion.

1. Interpret Diagrams Draw an arrow in the diagram to show the direction in which the ice is moving. Draw an *X* where you think abrasion is occurring. Draw a circle where plucking is happening.
2. SEP Construct Explanations In your own words, describe the glacial erosion taking place in the diagram.

Glacial Erosion The movement of a glacier slowly changes the land beneath it. The two processes by which glaciers erode the land are plucking and abrasion.

As a glacier flows over the land, it picks up rocks in a process called **plucking**. The weight of the ice breaks rocks into fragments that freeze to the bottom of the glacier. Then the rock fragments get carried with the glacier, as shown in **Figure 2**. Plucking leaves behind a jagged landscape.

Many rocks remain embedded on the bottom and sides of the glacier, and the glacier drags them across the land much like sandpaper in a process called abrasion. Land is worn away and deep gouges and scratches form in the bedrock.

For most glaciers, advancing, retreating, and eroding the land are very slow events. It can take years for scientists to observe any change in a glacier or its effects. Sometimes, however, glaciers move unusually fast. In 2012, scientists determined that a glacier in Greenland advanced up to 46 meters per day, faster than any other glacier recorded.

Although glaciers move and work slowly, they are a major force of erosion. They can take years to carve tiny scratches in bedrock. They can also carve out huge valleys hundreds of kilometers long over thousands of years. Through slow movement and erosion, glaciers dramatically change the shape of large areas of Earth's surface.

INTERACTIVITY

Examine water's effect on glaciers.

Glacial Deposition A glacier carries large amounts of rock and soil as it erodes the land in its path. As the glacier melts, it deposits the sediment it eroded from the land, creating various landforms, detailed in **Figure 3**. These landforms remain for thousands of years after the glacier has melted. The mixture of sediments that a glacier deposits directly on the surface is called **till**, which includes clay, silt, sand, gravel, boulders, and even rock ground so finely it is called rock flour.

Moraine The till deposited at the edges of a glacier forms a ridge called a moraine. Lateral moraines are deposits of sediment along the sides of a glacier. A terminal moraine is the ridge of till that is dropped at the farthest point reached by a glacier.

Landforms of Glacial Erosion and Deposition

Figure 3 Glacial erosion and deposition wear down and build up Earth's surface, producing landforms.

Classify In the model of a landscape shaped by glaciers, identify the features of erosion and deposition. In the circles, write *E* for erosion and *D* for deposition.

Horn When glaciers carve away the sides of a mountain, the result is a sharpened peak called a horn.

Cirque A cirque is a bowl-shaped hollow eroded by a glacier.

Moraine A moraine is a ridge that forms where a glacier deposits till.

Fjord A fjord forms when the level of the sea rises, filling a valley once cut by a glacier.

Arête An arête is a sharp ridge separating two cirques.

Kettle Retreating, or melting, glaciers also create features called kettles. A kettle is a steep-sided depression that forms when a chunk of ice is left in glacial till. When the ice melts, the kettle remains. The continental glacier of the last ice age left behind many kettles. Kettles often fill with water, forming small ponds or lakes called kettle lakes. Such lakes are common in areas such as Wisconsin that were once covered with glaciers.

CHECK POINT **Write Informative Texts** What are the effects of glacial deposition?

....

....

....

....

Model It!

SEP Develop Models In the space provided, draw part of the same landscape to show what the surface looked like before glacial erosion and deposition.

U-Shaped valley A flowing glacier scoops out a U-shaped valley.

Kettle lake A kettle lake forms when a depression left in till by melting ice fills with water.

uInvestigate Explore coastline erosion.

Waves Change Earth's Surface

Like glaciers, water waves change Earth's surface. The energy in most waves comes from the wind. Stronger winds cause larger waves. The friction between the wave and the ocean floor slows the wave. Then the water breaks powerfully on the shore. This provides the force that changes the shoreline.

Wave Erosion Waves shape the coast through weathering and erosion by breaking down rock and moving sand and other sediments. Large waves can hit rocks along the shore with great force, or **impact**. Over time, waves can enlarge cracks in rocks and cause pieces of rock to break off. Waves also break apart rocks by abrasion. As a wave reaches shallow water, it picks up and carries sediment, including sand and gravel. When the wave hits land, the sediment wears away rock.

Academic Vocabulary

How might you use the word *impact* in everyday life? Write a sentence using the word.

....

....

....

....

....

Waves approaching the shore gradually change direction as different parts of the waves drag on the bottom, as shown in **Figure 4**. The energy of these waves is concentrated on headlands. A headland is a part of the shore that extends into the ocean. Gradually, soft rock erodes, leaving behind the harder rock that is resistant to wave erosion. But over time, waves erode the headlands and even out the shoreline.

Humans can fight wave erosion by building artificial barriers such as jetties and sea walls that block wave energy from reaching shore. But some human activities, such as removing sand from beaches to use in construction, mimics the effects of wave erosion.

Headland Erosion

Figure 4 Wave erosion wears away rock to form headlands.

1. SEP Develop Models Shade in the arrows that indicate where waves concentrate the greatest amount of energy.
2. CCC Cause and Effect Draw a line to show how continued erosion will change the shoreline.
3. CCC Stability and Change How does this model help you understand a system or process of change?

....

....

....

....

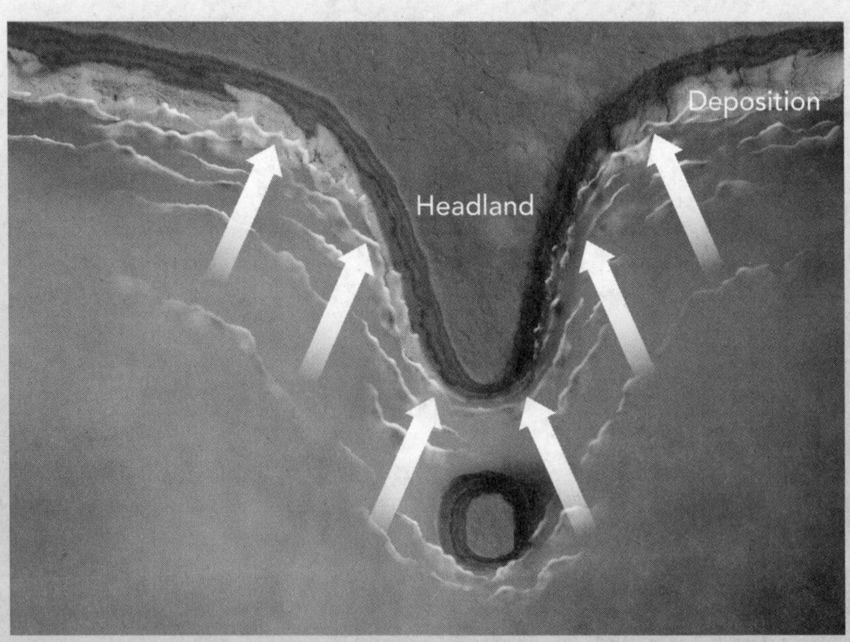

Landforms Formed by Wave Erosion When an axe strikes the base of a tree trunk, the cut gets bigger and deeper with each strike. Similarly, when ocean waves hit a steep, rocky coast, they erode the base of the land. Waves erode the softer rock first. Over time, the waves may erode a hollow notch in the rock called a sea cave. Eventually, waves may erode the base of a cliff so much that the cliff collapses. The rubble is washed out by wave action and the result is a wave-cut platform at the cliff's base, which is all that remains of the eroded cliff. A sea arch is another feature of wave erosion that forms when waves erode a layer of softer rock that underlies a layer of harder rock. If an arch collapses, a pillar of rock called a sea stack may result.

Wave erosion changes Earth's surface at different rates. Sometimes it changes the land quickly. During a single powerful storm with strong winds that form high-energy waves, part of a cliff or sea stack may crumble. Waves may pick up and carry away large amounts of sediment along a shore. In general, waves erode rock slowly, cutting cliffs and headlands back centimeters to meters in a year. Waves may take hundreds to thousands of years to wear away headlands and even out shorelines.

CHECK POINT **Write Explanatory Texts** Reread the text. Then explain how you think a sea cave might become a sea arch.

....

....

Landforms Formed by Wave Erosion

Figure 5 Label the landform formed by wave erosion on Anacapa Island, one of the Channels Islands off California's coast. Then draw dotted lines to indicate what new landforms could be produced if wave erosion continues.

Literacy Connection

Write Informative Texts

As you read, think about how you could help another student understand the concepts. Then, in your own words, describe how waves cause erosion.

....

....

....

....

....

....

....

INTERACTIVITY

Investigate wind and water erosion in Florida.

Wave Deposition Deposition occurs when waves lose energy and slow down, causing the water to drop the sediment it carries. Waves change the shape of a coast when they deposit sediment and form landforms.

Landforms Formed by Wave Deposition A beach is an area of wave-washed sediment along a coast. The sediment deposited on beaches is usually sand. Some sand is made of tiny fragments of rock, while other types are made of the shells of tiny marine organisms and broken pieces of coral.

Waves usually hit the beach at an angle, creating a current that runs parallel to the coastline. As waves repeatedly hit the beach, some of the sediment gets carried along the beach with the current, in a process called **longshore drift**.

Longshore drift also builds up sandbars and creates barrier islands. Sandbars are long ridges of sand parallel to the shore. A spit is an extended part of a beach that is connected by one end to the mainland. A barrier island forms when waves pile up large amounts of sand above sea level, forming a long, narrow island parallel to the coast. Barrier islands are found in numerous other places along the Atlantic coast of the United States. Barrier islands are constantly changing from wave erosion and deposition that occur during hurricanes and other storms.

CHECK POINT **Translate Information** Use the information in the text and **Figure 6** to determine how the coastline might change if large amounts of sand built up higher than sea level as a result of storm deposition.

....

Landforms Formed by Wave Deposition

Figure 6 On the diagram, draw arrows and label them to show the direction of longshore drift and the flow of sediment from the river to the sea.

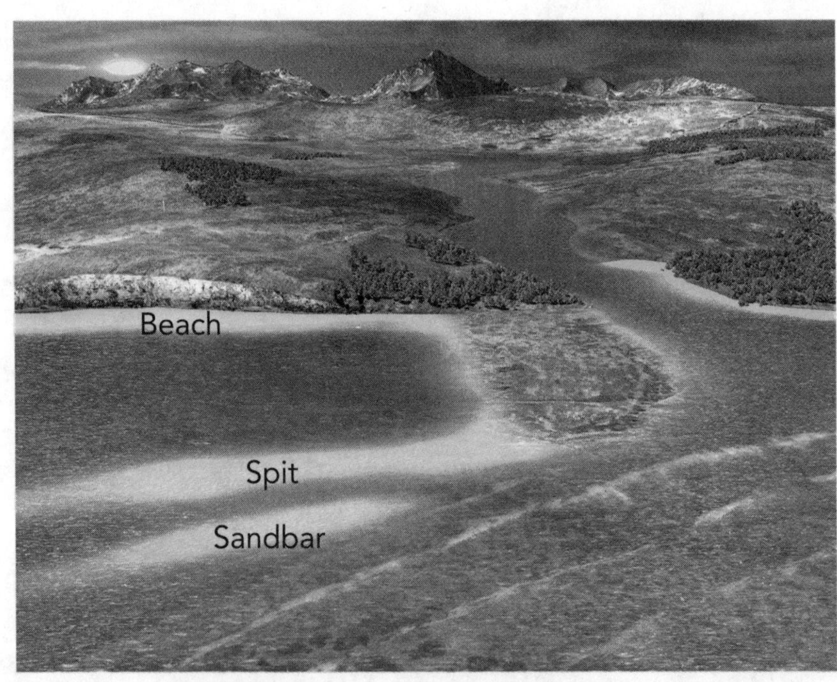

LESSON 4 Check

MS-ESS2-2, EP&CIc

1. **Identify** What are three landforms formed by wave deposition?

The three land forms formed by wave deposition are beaches, spirs, and ~~bars~~ sandbars.

2. **CCC Stability and Change** How are the ways in which glaciers and waves wear down Earth's surface similar? Use "scale" in your answer.

Waves wear down the Earth's surface by the waves hitting them with a great force. Glaciers wear down Earth's by ~~eroding~~ depositing sediments such as soil clay. ~~which then~~ Then when glacier melts it creates various landforms.

3. **CCC Cause and Effect** A valley in the Rocky Mountains contains a glacier. How might the glacier change this valley in the future?

The Glacier, as it melts, it ~~drop~~ deposits sediments such as clay, soil, or silt. This can create various other landforms.

4. **SEP Develop Models** Draw and label diagrams to show how a sea arch might form from a headland.

Arch

wave

wave

Quest CHECK-IN

In this lesson, you discovered how erosion and deposition by glaciers change Earth's surface. You also learned how erosion and deposition by waves change Earth's surface.

CCC System Models Why is it important to consider the effects of wave erosion and deposition when designing an artificial island?

INTERACTIVITY

Breaking Waves

Go online to examine how wave erosion might impact the location of your island, and adjust your design as needed.

LESSON 5

Severe Weather and Floods

HANDS-ON LAB

uInvestigate Record and analyze historical hurricane data to predict future events.

MS-ESS3-2 Analyze and interpret data on natural hazards to forecast future catastrophic events and inform the development of technologies to mitigate their effects. (Also **EP&CIIIa, EP&CIIIb**)

Connect It!

Label the center, or eye, of this North Atlantic hurricane.

SEP Analyze Data In what direction are the winds swirling around the location you identified?

....

Predict How might this storm affect people living near its path?

....

....

Types of Severe Storms

In October 2016, Hurricane Matthew struck the Caribbean and the southeastern United States with torrential rains and winds that reached **approximate** speeds of 250 km/h. Shown in the satellite image in **Figure 1**, it was one of the most intense storms ever to hit that part of the United States.

The death toll due to Hurricane Matthew surpassed 1000, with most of those deaths occurring in Haiti. In the United States, approximately 40 people died, more than half of these in North Carolina. Florida did not receive the extremely strong winds that some areas did, but the hurricane dropped between 7 and 10 inches of rain in the eastern half of the state. Property damage from the hurricane was extreme. Many areas were battered by winds or flooded for days. Many buildings were blown down and roads were eroded.

A hurricane is one example of a storm. A **storm** is a violent disturbance in the atmosphere. Storms involve sudden changes in air pressure, which cause rapid air movements and often precipitation. There are several types of severe storms: winter storms, thunderstorms, hurricanes, and tornadoes. These storms can be natural disasters on their own and also contribute to natural disasters related to Earth's surface processes. Rain and high winds associated with these storms can contribute to weathering, erosion, and mass movement such as landslides and mudflows.

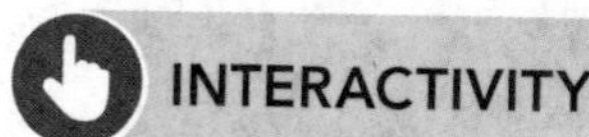

Write about your experiences with severe weather.

Academic Vocabulary

What is the difference between an approximate and an exact number?

....

....

....

Hurricane Matthew

Figure 1 This satellite image shows Hurricane Matthew swirling north of Cuba in the Caribbean Sea.

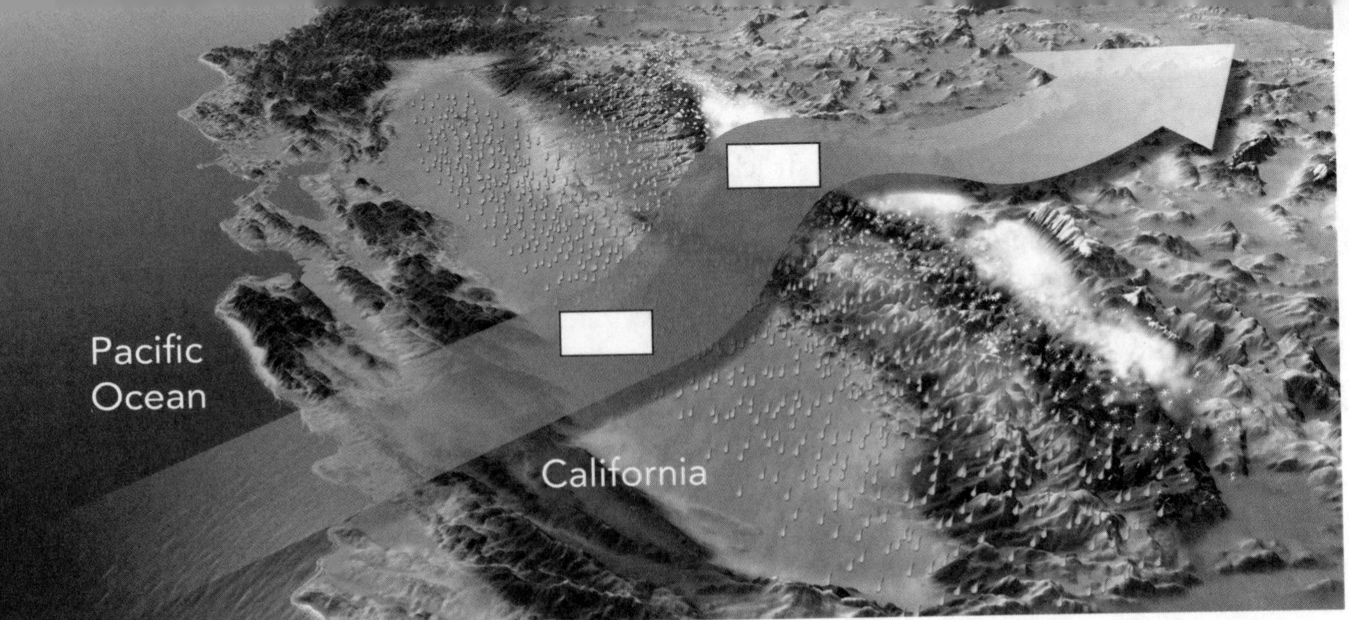

Atmospheric River

Figure 2 This map depicts an atmospheric river carrying huge amounts of moisture from tropical areas of the Pacific Ocean to California. Fill in the boxes with what you think the air temperatures would be based on the types of precipitation that are occurring there.

Write About It Identify the actions you can take to remain safe during a severe storm of any kind.

Winter Storms Precipitation that falls in the northern United States often occurs in the form of snow. Snow forms if the air is colder than 0°C between a cloud and the ground. If the ground is also cold, snow can accumulate and block roads, trap people in their homes, and cause other problems.

Locations that are downwind from large bodies of water often receive more snow than other locations. This effect, which is known as the lake effect in areas of the northeast, is due to the relative warmth of these bodies of water, and the large amounts of moisture they release through evaporation. When a cold, dry air mass moves across a lake, such as Lake Erie of the Great Lakes, it picks up water vapor and heat. When the air mass reaches the cold shore, it cools, causing the moist air to condense in large clouds that develop into snow.

A similar phenomenon can produce dramatic winter precipitation near the ocean, as shown in **Figure 2.** In California, warm, moist air masses flow in from tropical areas of the Pacific Ocean, bringing rain or snow. This phenomenon can transport as much water as the Mississippi River, but because the river is made of water vapor it is known as an "atmospheric river." In early 2017, areas of the Sierra Nevada Mountains received ten feet of snow in just one week, due to an atmospheric river.

Heavy snowfall can be deadly. Snow-covered roads are slippery, causing automobile accidents. Snow can fall so quickly, in what is called "white out" conditions, that rescue vehicles cannot even reach people whose cars have skidded off roadways. Roofs of buildings and power lines can collapse under the weight of heavy snow. The physical damage caused by a winter snowstorm, or blizzard, can be compounded by the economic toll of missed workdays, shut-down schools, and cleanup and rebuilding. On the other hand, some industries, such as ski resorts, thrive on heavy snowfall. Heavy precipitation in winter can also replenish bodies of water on land, from lakes to river to aquifers.

Thunderstorms Spring and summer are often associated with clear, warm weather, but they are also the times when hazardous thunderstorms can form.

A **thunderstorm** is a localized storm often accompanied by heavy precipitation, frequent thunder, and dangerous lightning. It forms when warm air carrying lots of moisture is forced upward along a cold front. The warm, humid air rises rapidly, forming dense thunderheads. Thunderstorms can bring heavy rain and hail.

During a thunderstorm, positive and negative electrical charges build up and discharge in the thunderheads. Lightning occurs as these charges jump between parts of a cloud, between nearby clouds, or between a cloud and the ground, all of which are shown in **Figure 3**.

The terrifying booms of thunder that can keep us up at night are produced when lightning heats the air near it to as much as 30,000°C. That's hotter than the sun's surface! The rapidly heated air expands explosively, creating the shockwave we call thunder in the surrounding air as it is compressed.

Thunderstorms cause severe damage. Their heavy rains may flood low-lying areas. This can cause erosion, landslides, and mudflows. Large hailstones ruin crops, damage property such as cars and windows, and may even cause fatalities to people and animals out in the open. Lightning strikes start fires and damage structures or sometimes just the electrical equipment within a structure. If lightning strikes a person, it can cause unconsciousness, serious burns, and even death.

Thunder and Lightning
Figure 3 Lightning strikes can cause severe damage during thunderstorms.

Model It!

How Thunderstorms Form

SEP Develop Models Draw a labeled diagram to show the formation of a thunderstorm.

Hurricanes When a cyclone's winds exceed 119 km/h, we call it a hurricane. A **hurricane** can stretch more than 600 kilometers across and it may have winds as strong as 320 km/h. In the western Pacific Ocean, these storms are called typhoons. When they occur in the Indian Ocean, they are known simply as cyclones.

A typical hurricane that strikes the United States forms in the Atlantic Ocean north of the equator during the late summer. It begins as a low-pressure area, or tropical disturbance, over ocean water warmed by solar radiation.

A hurricane draws its energy from the warm, humid air near the warm ocean's surface. This air rises, forming clouds and drawing surrounding air into the area, as shown in **Figure 4**. Bands of heavy rains and high winds spiral inward toward the area of lowest pressure at the center. The lower the air pressure at the center of the storm, the faster the winds blow toward it.

Hurricane winds are strongest in a narrow band or ring of clouds at the storm's center called the eyewall, which encloses the storm's "eye." When the eye arrives, the weather changes suddenly, growing calm and clear. After the eye passes, the storm resumes, but the winds blow from the opposite direction.

Hurricanes often result in severe flooding, which in turn contaminates drinking water supplies. Flooding and wind damage can also lead to erosion, landslides, and mudflows, which can make travel after the storm difficult. Residents of hurricane-prone areas are encouraged to stock a three-day supply of drinking water, ready-to-eat food, and any other necessary items, such as medications or diapers, to help them through the aftermath of a hurricane.

Literacy Connection

Cite Textual Evidence
Textual evidence is information or clues that reinforce or support an idea. Reread the third and fourth paragraphs on this page. Underline the evidence that supports the statement that hurricane winds are strongest around the storm's center.

Formation of a Hurricane

Figure 4 ✎ Draw arrows to show how warm, humid air rises to form clouds and how winds spiral toward the area of low pressure.

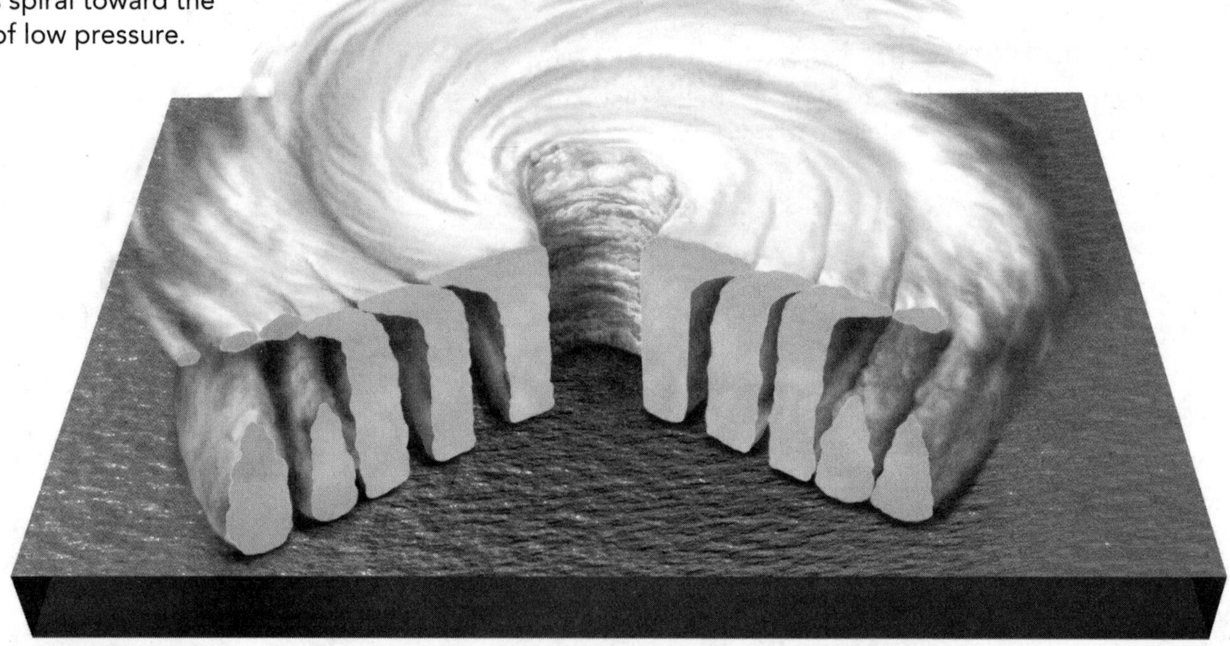

Topic 9 Lesson 4 Notes

Glacial and Wave Erosion

- Glaciers change Earth's surface
  - Glacier
    - Any larger mass of ice that moves slowly overland
    - Occur in cold regions where more snow fall melts
    - Glaciers play role in the weathering, erosion, and deposition
  - Continental glaciers
    - A glacier that covers much of a continent or large scale
    - Ice Ages
      - Continental glaciers covered much more of earth's crust
  - Change the shape of Earth
  - Valley glacier
    - A long narrow glacier that forms when snow builds up in mountain in valleys
    - Put downhill by gravity
  - Plucking
    - the process of glaciers picking up rocks as it moves
  - Till
    - the mixture of sediment glaciers deposit onthe surface
  - Wave erosion
    - Waves shape coastlines
    - waves in shallow water picks up sediment
    - that sediment gets carried to the Shorre line and wears away at rocks
    - soft rock erodes and will leave behind harder rocck

- land forms formed by wind erosion
  - Slow process
  - talking hundreds thousands of years
- Wave Deposition
  - longshore drift
    - a wave repeatedly hits a beach and some sediment gets carried along the beach with the current

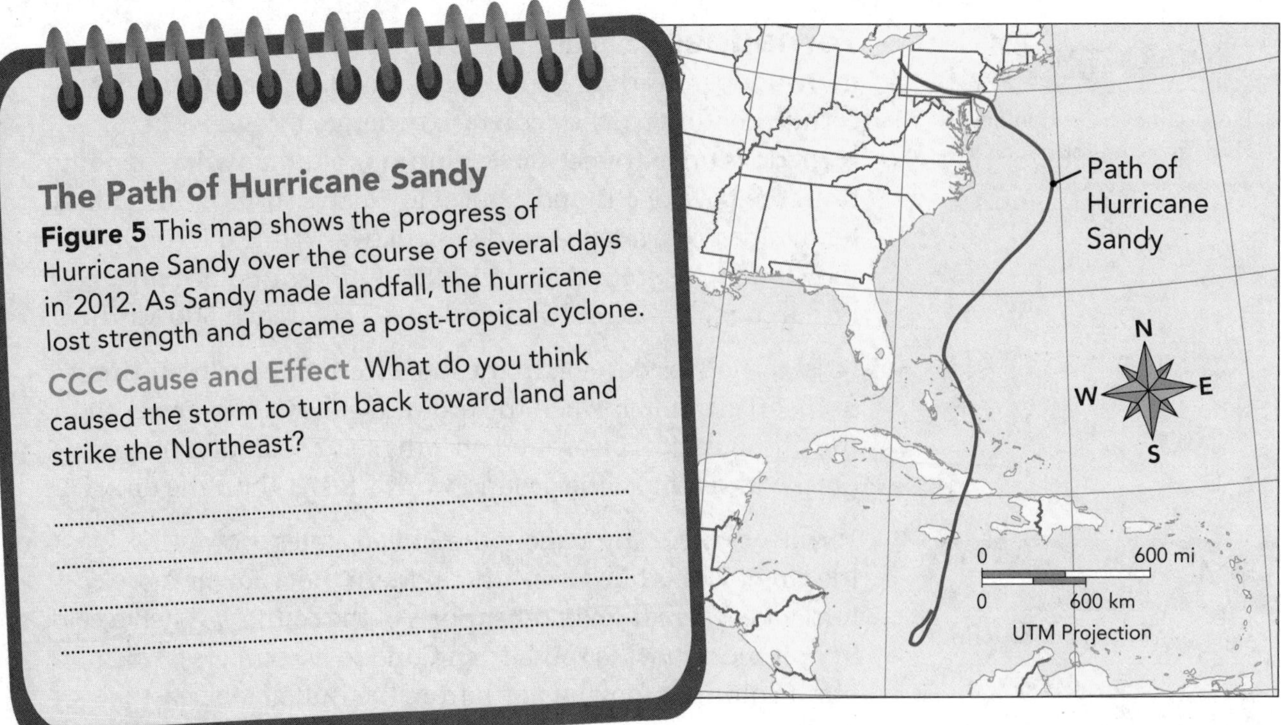

The Path of Hurricane Sandy

Figure 5 This map shows the progress of Hurricane Sandy over the course of several days in 2012. As Sandy made landfall, the hurricane lost strength and became a post-tropical cyclone.

CCC Cause and Effect What do you think caused the storm to turn back toward land and strike the Northeast?

How Hurricanes Move Hurricanes are long-lasting storms, existing for a week or more. They can travel thousands of kilometers from where they originally formed. Hurricanes that form in the Atlantic Ocean are usually steered by easterly trade winds toward the Caribbean islands and then up toward the southeastern and eastern United States, as was Hurricane Sandy in 2012 (**Figure 5**). Once a hurricane passes over land, it loses its energy source: warm, moist air. If the hurricane doesn't travel over another source of warm, moist air to fuel it, it will gradually weaken.

HANDS-ON LAB

Investigate Record and analyze historical hurricane data to predict future events.

When a hurricane makes landfall, high waves, severe flooding, and wind damage often accompany it. Massive erosion, land-slides, and mudflows are also common. A hurricane's low pressure and high winds can raise the level of the water in the ocean below it by as much as 6 meters above normal sea level. The result is a **storm surge**, a "dome" of water that sweeps across the coast where the hurricane is traveling. Storm surges can cause great damage, destroying human-made structures as well as coastal ecosystems.

VIRTUAL LAB

Investigate conditions that form hurricanes.

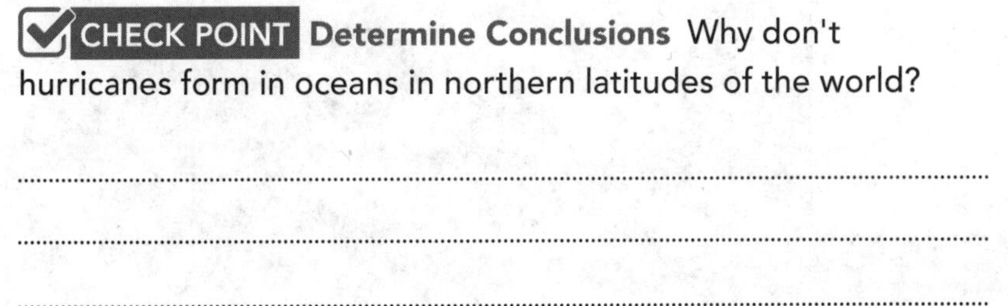

CHECK POINT **Determine Conclusions** Why don't hurricanes form in oceans in northern latitudes of the world?

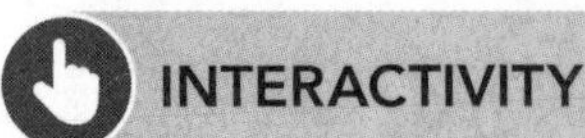

Determine the conditions that favor the formation of tornadoes.

Tornadoes Thunderstorms can lead to something even more dangerous than heavy rains, flooding, or hail. Under certain conditions, they can also generate tornadoes. A **tornado** is an extremely fast spinning column of air extending from the base of a thunderstorm to Earth's surface. Tornadoes tend to be brief, intense, and destructive. While a tornado may touch the ground for 15 minutes or less and be only a few hundred meters across, its wind speed can reach 500 km/h.

Most tornadoes develop in the late afternoon during spring and early summer, when the ground tends to be warmer than the air above it. The ground absorbs solar radiation more quickly than air so the ground warms faster than the air.

VIDEO

Watch how tornadoes form.

Tornadoes occur throughout the United States. However, the Great Plains have a weather pattern that spawns more tornadoes there than in other parts of the country. When a cold, dry air mass moving south from Canada encounters a warm, humid air mass moving north from the Gulf of Mexico, the colder, denser air pushes under the warmer air mass, forcing it to rise. Warm ground can "turbo-charge" this process by releasing some of the heat it absorbed from the sun. This extra heat forces the air above to rise even faster. An area of low pressure develops and rapidly draws surrounding air inward and up. This fast-moving air rotates as it rises and forms a funnel. If the funnel touches Earth's surface, it becomes a tornado.

Tornado damage comes from both strong winds and the flying debris those winds carry. Tornadoes can move large objects and scatter debris many miles away. To reduce the possibility of being injured during a tornado, above ground concrete storm shelters, in-home safe rooms, or below ground storm shelters are designed to protect the occupants. The Fujita Scale, shown in **Figure 6**, allows meteorologists to categorize tornadoes based on the amount and type of damage they cause.

Tornado Damage

Figure 6 Only about one percent of tornadoes are ranked as F4 or F5. In 2007, the original Fujita Scale was replaced by the Enhanced Fujita Scale to more closely align high wind speeds with the types of damage they typically cause to structures.

✎ Use the image to rate the damage shown by circling a rating on the Fujita Scale.

Fujita Scale	Types of Damage
F0	Branches broken off trees
F1	Mobile homes overturned
F2	Trees uprooted
F3	Roofs torn off
F4	Houses leveled
F5	Houses carried away

Floods and Drought

Storms are not the only type of hazardous severe weather. Floods, droughts, and excessive heat can occur in many different areas in the United States.

California Flooding

Figure 7 In 2017, heavy rainfall caused flooding in many areas of California. Neighborhoods in San Jose, pictured here, suffered extensive damage.

Floods Flooding is a major danger during severe storms, such as the one shown in **Figure 7**. A **flood** is an overflowing of water in a normally dry area. Some floods occur when excess water from rain or melting snow overflows a stream or river. In urban areas, floods occur when the ground can't absorb any water because it is already saturated. Flooding can cause severe erosion, landslides, and mudflows.

Dams and levees are used to control flooding near rivers. A dam is a barrier across a river that may redirect the flow of the river or store floodwaters so that they can be released slowly. An embankment built along a river to prevent flooding of the surrounding land is a levee.

Droughts and Excessive Heat Having too little water can also cause problems. A long period with little or no rainfall is known as a **drought**. Drought is caused by hot, dry weather systems that stay in one place for weeks or months at a time. Long-term droughts can lead to crop failures and wildfires. Reservoirs are large natural or man-made lakes that are used to store water for human use to help minimize the impact of a drought. Streams, reservoirs, and wells dry up, causing shortages of water for homes, businesses, plants, and animals. People can help lessen the impacts of drought by conserving water.

Heat waves can also be harmful to people. Prolonged exposure to heat and the sun can cause skin damage, heat stroke, and dehydration. To prevent overexposure to the sun, wear protective clothing, sunglasses, and sunscreen, and avoid direct sunlight between the hours of 10 am and 2 pm.

CHECK POINT **Cite Textual Evidence** What are two ways to help prevent floods?

....

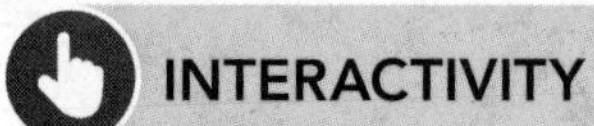

Examine the technologies used to predict and mitigate the effects of severe weather.

Storm Safety

When potentially dangerous storms are likely, weather announcements indicate where there is a storm "watch" and where there is a storm "warning." A watch means that conditions are right for producing severe weather, but the severe weather has not yet developed. A warning signifies that severe weather is approaching and people should take shelter. **Figure 8** shows the precautions people should take for each type of severe storm.

Severe Storm Safety

Figure 8 Different severe storms require different safety measures.

Tornado If you hear a tornado warning, go to a safe area quickly. Move to the middle of the ground floor. Stay away from windows and doors.

Winter Storm Winter storms can limit your vision and make it easy to get lost. Strong winds cool bodies rapidly. Stay or get indoors and keep a supply of water and food on hand in case of a power outage.

Thunderstorm Get and stay indoors. If in a car, it's safe to stay there. But if you are outside, find a low area away from trees, fences, and poles. If you are swimming or in a boat, get to shore and find shelter.

Hurricane Today, weather satellites can track and warn people well in advance of an approaching hurricane. You should be prepared to evacuate, or move away temporarily. If you hear a hurricane warning and are told to evacuate, leave the area immediately.

CHECK POINT **Determine Central Ideas** What safety precautions are common to all types of severe weather?

....

....

LESSON 5 Check

MS-ESS3-2, EP&CIIIa, EP&CIIIb

1. **Identify** What are four types of severe storms?

The four serve storms are Tornados Winter Storms, Thunderstorms, and Hurricanes

2. **SEP Develop Solutions** For communities in areas where flooding or droughts have occurred and are predicted to occur again, what are some ways communities can mitigate, or reduce the effects of these events?

Dams and levees control the rivers to not flood. But having little water can cause droughts.

3. **Draw Conclusions** When hurricanes or thunderstorms strike, damage from the floods they may produce can last much longer than the storms themselves. Why do floods cause damage for longer periods of time?

This is because flooding can cause mudflows, landslides, and erosion.

4. **SEP Develop Models** Assume a tornado warning has been issued for where you live. Draw a diagram of your home and show an example of a technology that could be used to keep you safe during a tornado. Then, beneath your diagram, explain why that location would be safe.

This is because the technology can cause a warning alert a were it is soon that you can escape.

MS-ESS2-2, MS-ESS3-2

Evidence-Based Assessment

A team of researchers is studying a massive landslide that occurred on the scenic stretch of California's coast known as Big Sur on May 20, 2017. Millions of tons of rock and dirt collapsed down a seaside slope onto the highway and spilled into the sea.

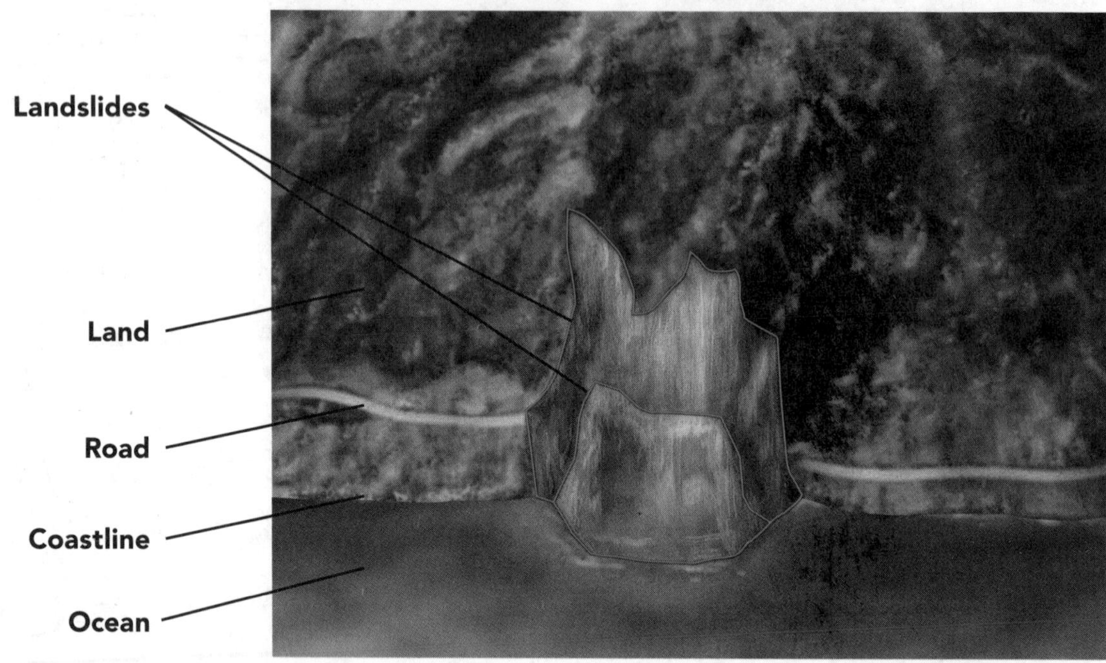

To understand what happened in Big Sur, researchers are analyzing average winter precipitation data collected over a thirty-year period. The data is displayed in the graph. The solid line across the middle of the graph marks the mean, or average, winter precipitation for California over the entire thirty-year period.

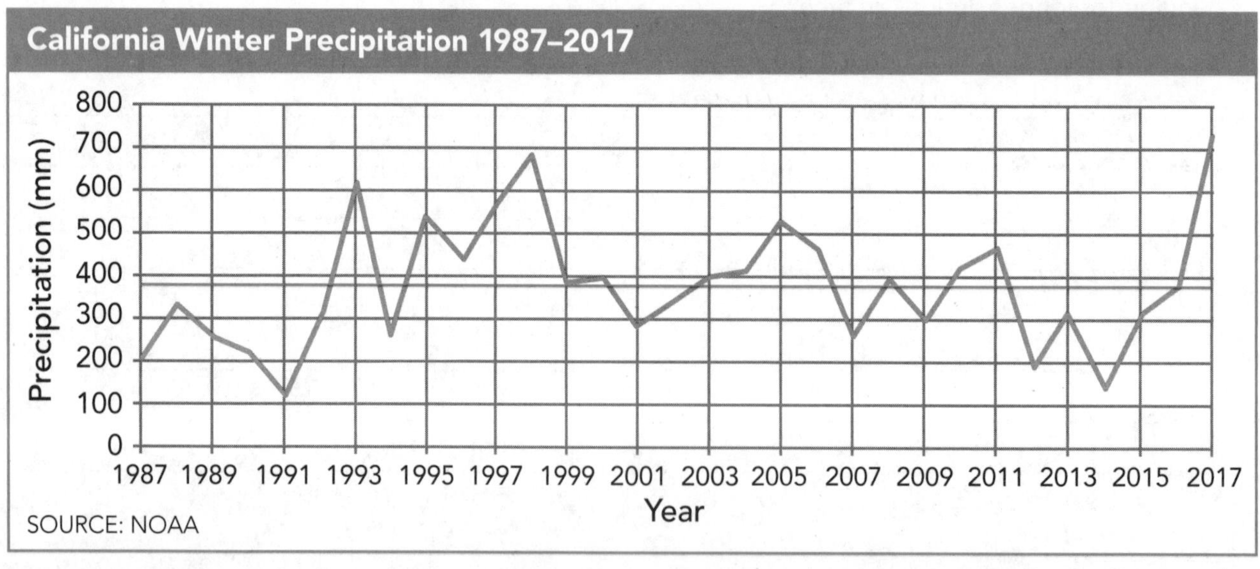

1. **SEP Analyze Data** How much precipitation did California receive in the winter prior to the May 20 landslide of 2017?

   A. 710 mm B. 390 mm
   C. 520 mm D. 800 mm

2. **SEP Interpret Data** How would you describe California's precipitation in the five winters prior to 2017? Select all the statements that apply.

   - ☐ It was above average for the five winters.
   - ☐ It was below average for four winters, and average for one.
   - ☐ It was below average for the five winters.
   - ☐ It was mostly above average.
   - ☐ It was mostly below average.
   - ☐ It was above average for four winters, and below average for one.

3. **CCC Stability and Change** In the image of the coast at Big Sur, what are three visible indications that a large landslide occurred?

   ....
   ....
   ....
   ....
   ....
   ....
   ....
   ....

4. **CCC Cause and Effect** How do you think weathering and erosion will affect the base of the deposited sediment, which is in the ocean? How will this affect the coastline in the future?

   ....
   ....
   ....
   ....
   ....
   ....
   ....

5. **SEP Construct Explanations** Predict the order in which the events leading up to the landside took place by placing the following steps in order from 1 to 4, with 1 being the first event and 4 being the last.

When the hillside got drier, the loosened soil crumbled and triggered a landslide.	....
Over 700 mm of rain fell in the winter of 2017.	....
The hillside was very dry due to five years of little rain.	....
The soil became saturated with water and loosened.	....

Quest FINDINGS

Complete the Quest!

Reflect on how changes to Earth's surface will impact an artificial island. Then, prepare and deliver an oral or written presentation explaining your island design and your model.

CCC System Models What are three things you learned about the processes that shape Earth's surface that helped you to design your artificial island?

....
....
....
....
....
....

INTERACTIVITY

Reflect on Your Ingenious Island

uDemonstrate Lab

MS-ESS2-2, MS-ESS3-2

Materials on a Slope

How can you use a **model** to determine the likelihood of **mass movement**?

Background

Phenomenon Geoscience processes such as rapid mass movement result in large amounts of sediment moving down hillsides.

In this investigation, you will work as part of a landslide monitoring team. You will develop and use a model to explore the relationship between the height and width of a hill. You will gain understanding about how these factors affect the hill's stability and the likelihood that mass movement will occur.

Safety

Be sure to follow all safety guidelines provided by your teacher. The Safety Appendix of your textbook provides more details about the safety icons.

Materials

(per group)

- tray (about 15 cm × 45 cm × 60 cm)
- several sheets of white paper
- masking tape
- cardboard tube
- spoon or paper cup
- dry sand (500 mL) in container
- wooden skewer
- metric ruler
- pencil or crayon
- graph paper

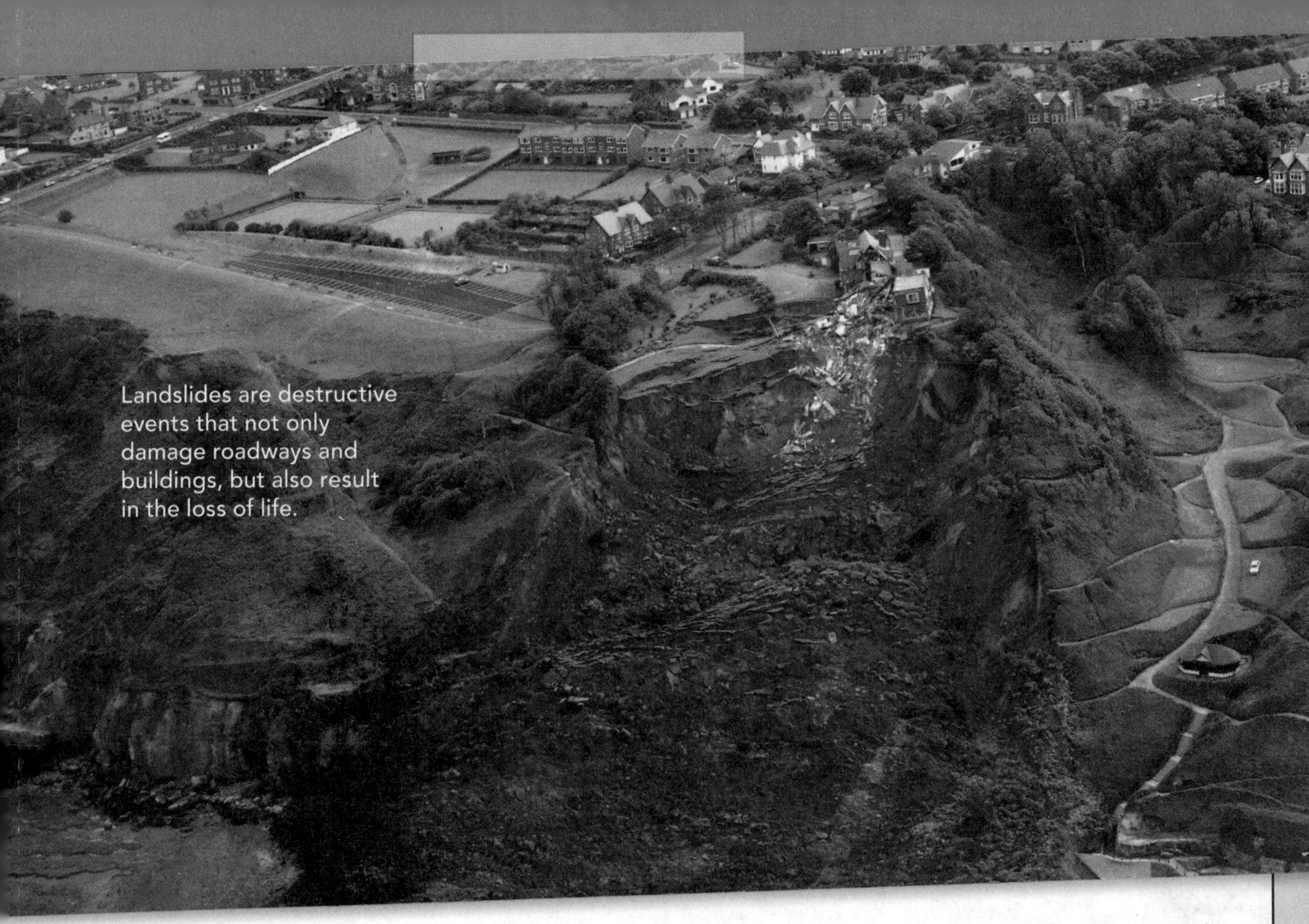

Landslides are destructive events that not only damage roadways and buildings, but also result in the loss of life.

Plan Your Investigation

- [ ] Use the metric ruler to mark off centimeters across the length of the paper. Take the tray provided by your teacher and use the paper to cover its interior surface. Secure the paper with tape. In the middle of the tray, stand the cardboard tube upright. Use a spoon or cup to fill the tube with sand.
- [ ] When the tube is nearly full, slowly and steadily pull the tube straight up so that the sand falls out of the bottom and forms a cone-shaped hill. Use different quantities of sand and observe the shapes and sizes of the sand hills created.
- [ ] Using the materials provided by your teacher, design an investigation to explore the relationship between the height and width of a sand hill. Determine how many sand hills you will create in your investigation.
- [ ] Then use the space provided to outline your procedure. Have your teacher review and approve your procedure, and then conduct your investigation. Create a data table to record your data about the heights and widths of the sand hills your group models.

HANDS-ON LAB

Demonstrate Go online for a downloadable worksheet of this lab.

Design Your Procedure

Data Table

Analyze and Interpret Data

1. **SEP Analyze Data** Study your data table. What patterns do you notice in your data?

2. **SEP Evaluate Information** What do your data suggest about the relationship between the height and width of a sand hill?

3. **SEP Identify Limitations** What are the advantages of using the sand hill model in this investigation? What are the limitations of using the model?

4. **CCC Scale, Proportion, and Quantity** How is your sand hill model similar to and different from a natural hill that undergoes mass movement?

5. **CCC Stability and Change** How could you apply the results of your investigation to help assess the likelihood of and forecast future mass movement events such as landslides? Use evidence from your investigation to support your explanation.

TOPIC 10

Populations, Communities, and Ecosystems

Investigative Phenomenon
How can changes to the physical or biological components of an ecosystem affect populations?

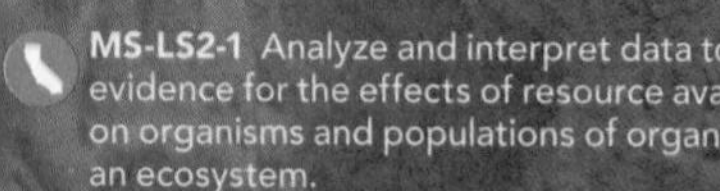

MS-LS2-1 Analyze and interpret data to provide evidence for the effects of resource availability on organisms and populations of organisms in an ecosystem.

MS-LS2-2 Construct an explanation that predicts patterns of interactions among organisms across multiple ecosystems.

MS-LS2-3 Develop a model to describe the cycling of matter and flow of energy among living and nonliving parts of an ecosystem.

MS-LS2-4 Construct an argument supported by empirical evidence that changes to physical or biological components of an ecosystem affect populations.

MS-LS2-5 Evaluate competing design solutions for maintaining biodiversity and ecosystem services.

EP&CIc Students should be developing an understanding that the quality, quantity, and reliability of the goods and ecosystem services provided by natural systems are directly affected by the health of those systems.

EP&CIIb Students should be developing an understanding that methods used to extract, harvest, transport, and consume natural resources influence the geographic extent, composition, biological diversity, and viability of natural systems.

EP&CIIIa Students should be developing an understanding that natural systems proceed through cycles and processes that are required for their functioning.

EP&CIIIb Students should be developing an understanding that human practices depend upon and benefit from the cycles and processes that operate within natural systems.

EP&CIIIc Students should be developing an understanding that human practices can alter the cycles and processes that operate within natural systems.

EP&CIVc Students should be developing an understanding that the capacity of natural systems to adjust to human-caused alterations depends on the nature of the system as well as the scope, scale, and duration of the activity and the nature of its byproducts.

EP&CVa Students should be developing an understanding of the spectrum of what is considered in making decisions about resources and natural systems and how those factors influence decisions.

Why would these deer risk crossing a busy road?

uConnect Explore how communities change in response to natural disasters.

What questions do you have about the phenomenon?

Quest PBL

Should an Animal Crossing Be Constructed in My Community?

STEM **Figure It Out** A company wants to build a new factory nearby, but wants the state to build a new highway to the location. The highway would allow employees and products to access the site. However, the highway would pass through an area with endangered species. Before the state decides, they contact a wildlife biologist to study the impact the highway would have on the local ecosystem. In this problem-based Quest activity, you will investigate how the construction of highways can affect organisms. By applying what you learn in each lesson, in a digital activity or hands-on lab, you will gather key Quest information and evidence. With the information, you will propose a solution in the Findings activity.

INTERACTIVITY

To Cross or Not to Cross

MS-LS2-4, MS-LS2-5, EP&CIIb, EP&CIIIa, EP&CIIIb, EP&CIIIc

NBC LEARN VIDEO

After watching the Quest kickoff video, where a wildlife biologist discusses animal crossings in Banff National Park, fill in the 3-2-1 activity.

3 organisms I think are at risk locally

....

....

....

2 ideas I have to help them

....

....

....

1 thing I learned from the wildlife biologist

....

....

....

Quest CHECK-IN

IN LESSON 1

How do animal crossings affect ecosystems? Analyze some effects then brainstorm ideas for your animal crossing and identify the criteria and constraints you need to consider.

INTERACTIVITY

Research Animal Crossings

Quest CHECK-IN

IN LESSON 2

How does community stakeholder feedback impact your design ideas, criteria, and constraints? Evaluate your design.

INTERACTIVITY

Community Opinions

Quest CHECK-IN

IN LESSON 3

STEM What are the criteria and constraints for the animal crossing? Evaluate competing design solutions.

HANDS-ON LAB

Design and Model a Crossing

This crossing over the highway looks like it is part of the surrounding forest. It's a much safer route for the animals, and keeps the drivers who pass underneath safe as well.

IN LESSON 4

How could a highway affect local ecosystem services? Consider your animal crossing design and how it might also affect ecosystem services.

Quest FINDINGS

Complete the Quest!

Determine the best way to clearly present your claim with data and evidence, such as graphics or a multimedia presentation.

INTERACTIVITY

Reflect on Your Animal Crossing

LESSON 1

Interactions in Ecosystems

HANDS-ON LAB

uInvestigate Model competition between organisms.

MS-LS2-1 Analyze and interpret data to provide evidence for the effects of resource availability on organisms and populations of organisms in an ecosystem.

MS-LS2-2 Construct an explanation that predicts patterns of interactions among organisms across multiple ecosystems. (Also **EP&CIIb**)

Connect It!

Outline the organism hidden in the image. What adaptations do you notice?

SEP Construct Explanations How do the animal's adaptations help it survive?

CCC Cause and Effect How does your body adapt to its environment?

Adaptations and Survival

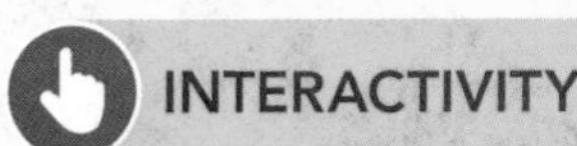

Identify competition in your daily life.

Each organism in an ecosystem has special characteristics. These characteristics influence whether an individual can survive and reproduce in its environment. A characteristic that makes an individual better suited to a specific environment may eventually become common in that species through a process called natural selection.

In this process, individuals with characteristics that are well-suited to a particular environment tend to survive and produce more offspring. Offspring inheriting these characteristics also are more likely to survive to reproduce. Natural selection results in adaptations—the behaviors and physical characteristics that allow organisms to live successfully in their environments. As an example, a great white shark's body is white along its underside, but dark across the top. The shark blends with the surroundings in the water whether being looked at from below or above. **Figure 1** shows another example of how a species adapts to its environment.

Individuals with characteristics that do not help them survive in their environments are less likely to reproduce. Over time, these unhelpful characteristics may affect the survival of a species. If individuals in a species cannot adapt successfully to changes in their environment, the species can become extinct.

Student Discourse
With a partner, discuss some ways that organisms in your local area have adapted to the environment. In your science notebook, describe characteristics that make the organism successful.

Adaptation and Survival

Figure 1 Different kinds of adaptations work together to aid in this Western screech owl's survival.

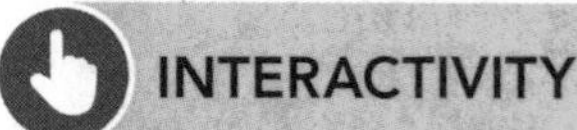

Model what competition looks like in nature.

Niche The organisms in any ecosystem have adaptations that help them fill specific roles or functions. The role of an organism in its habitat is called its niche. A niche includes how an organism obtains its food, the type of food the organism eats, and what other organisms eat it.

Remember that an organism's energy role in an ecosystem is determined by how it obtains food and how it interacts with other organisms. Adaptations by a species allow a population to live successfully on the available resources in its niche. Abiotic factors also influence a population's ability to survive in the niche it occupies. Lack of water or space, for example, may cause a population to decline and no longer fit well into that niche. Biotic factors, such as predators or a reduced food source, affect the populations in a niche and may change an organism's ability to survive.

A niche also includes when and how the organism reproduces and the physical conditions it requires to survive. Every organism has a variety of adaptations that suit it to specific living conditions and help it survive. Use **Figure 2** to describe characteristics of a giraffe's niche.

Niche Characteristics

Figure 2 This picture shows that organisms occupy many niches in an environment.

A Safari Guide's Q & A

I observed this giraffe in the wild during a group safari. Here are some questions I received. Can you answer them?

Relate Text to Visuals What does the feeding behavior of the giraffe tell you about its niche?

....

....

CHECK POINT **Determine Central Ideas** What adaptations might the giraffe have that help it survive in its environment?

....

....

Egret Wades into water to grab small fish.

Flamingo Feeds on tiny organisms on the muddy bottom.

Oystercatcher Uses its narrow beak to pry open shellfish.

Skimmer Nabs small fish on the surface of the water.

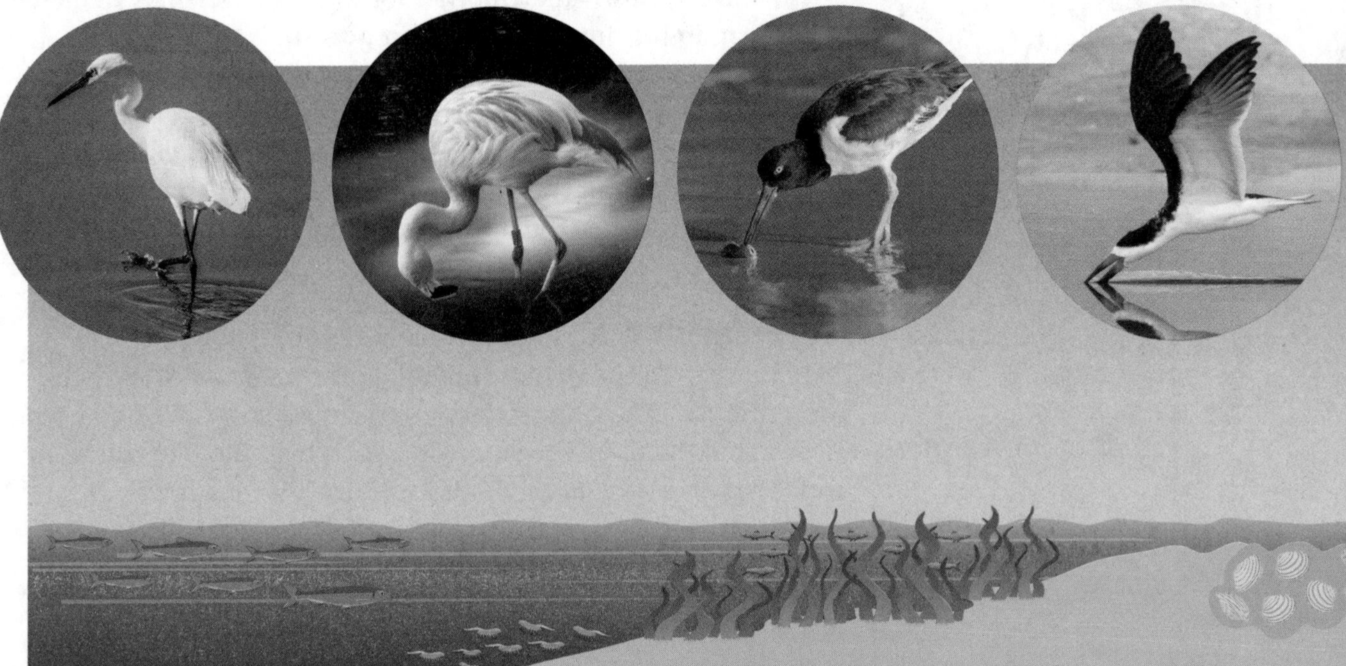

Shorebird Competition

Figure 3 ✎ Draw a line from each bird to the location where it feeds.

Competition and Predation

In every type of ecosystem, a range of **interactions** takes place among organisms every day. Two major types of interactions among organisms are competition and predation.

Competition More than one species of organism can live in the same habitat and obtain the same food. For example, in a desert ecosystem, a flycatcher and an elf owl both live on the saguaro cactus and eat insects. However, these two species do not occupy exactly the same niche. The flycatcher is active during the day, while the owl is active mostly at night.

When two species share a niche, one of their populations might be affected. The reason for this is **competition**. The struggle between organisms to survive as they use the same limited resources is called competition. For example, different species of birds in a park compete for the same bugs and worms to eat. If one population of birds is more successful, it will increase while the other population decreases.

In any ecosystem, there are limited amounts of food, water, and shelter. Organisms that share the same habitat often have adaptations that enable them to reduce competition. Observe the shorebirds in **Figure 3** and discover how their niches vary in the shoreline habitat.

Academic Vocabulary

How have you heard the term *interactions* used in another subject and what does the word mean in that context?

....

....

....

....

....

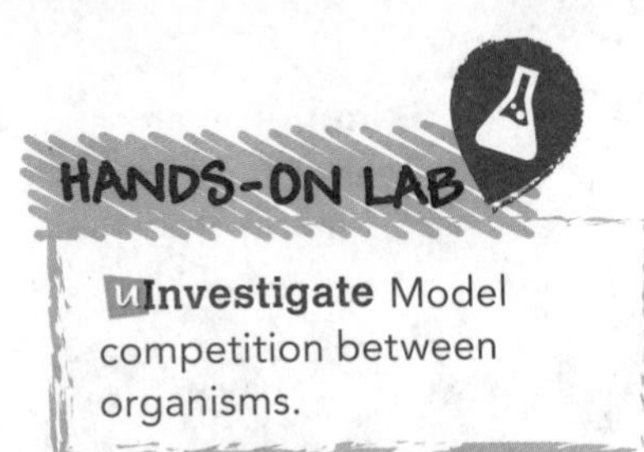

Investigate Model competition between organisms.

Predation A tiger shark bursts through the water and grabs a sea snake swimming on the surface. An interaction in which one organism kills another for food or nutrients is called **predation**. In this interaction, one organism is the predator and the other is the prey. The tiger shark, for example, is the predator and the sea snake is the prey. Predator and prey interactions occur in all ecosystems. The species involved may be different, but the pattern of interaction is the same. Predation can reduce the number of organisms or eliminate populations.

Adaptations All species have ways of supporting their survival in their environment. Some predators have adaptations, such as sharp teeth and claws, well-developed senses, and the ability to run fast, which help them to catch and kill their prey **(Figure 4)**. Prey organisms may have protective coverings, warning coloration, or the ability to camouflage themselves to help them avoid being killed.

Model It!

Predator and Prey Adaptations

Figure 4 In the Mojave Desert in California, the Mojave rattlesnake blends in with its surroundings so that it can ambush rodents it preys on. The snake's venom is considered to be the strongest rattlesnake venom in the world.

SEP Develop Models Consider a grassland ecosystem of tall, tan savanna grasses. Draw either a predator or a prey organism that might live there. Label the adaptations that will allow your organism to be successful.

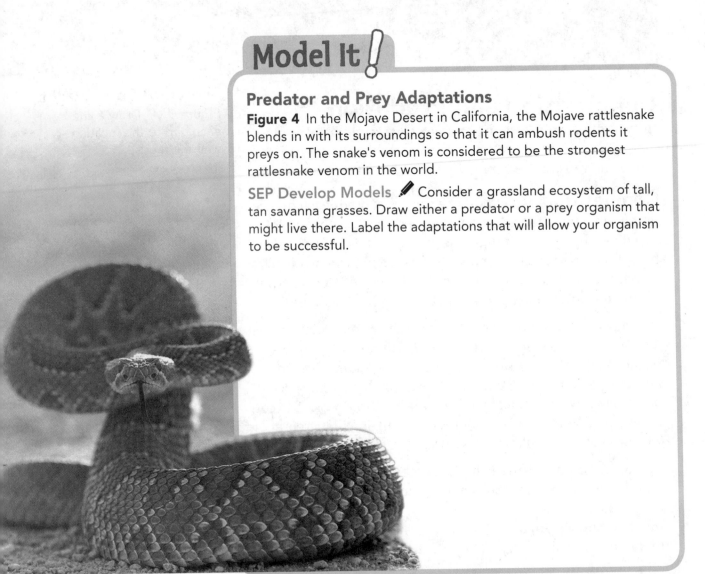

Population Size Predation affects population size. Changes in population size occur when new members arrive or when members leave. Population size increases if more members enter than leave, and declines if more members leave than arrive. Too many predators in a area can decrease the prey population, leading to less food availability and possible predator population decline. In general, predator and prey populations rise and fall together in predictable patterns.

CHECK POINT **Summarize Text** What effect do competition and predation have on population size?

....

....

Math Toolbox

Predator-Prey Interactions

Moose and Wolf

Populations on Isle Royale

On Isle Royale, an island in Lake Superior, the populations of wolves (the predator) and moose (the prey) rise and fall in cycles.

Year	Wolves	Moose
1985	22	976
1990	15	1,315
1995	16	2,117
2000	29	2,007
2005	30	540
2010	19	510
2015	2	1,300

1. **Construct Graphs** Create a double line graph of the data above. Fill in the x-axis and both y-axes. Use a different color line for each animal and provide a key.

2. **SEP Analyze and Interpret Data** Describe the relationship shown by your graph and suggest factors that impact it.

20
0
1985 1990
400

....

....

....

....

....

INTERACTIVITY

Classify symbiotic relationships.

VIDEO

Explore the three types of symbiotic relationships.

Academic Vocabulary

Break the adjective *interdependent* into two parts. Based on those word parts, what is an interdependent relationship among species?

....

....

....

....

....

Literacy Connection

Determine Central Ideas As you read, determine the central idea of the text. Note how this idea is developed through examples. Underline examples that you think most clearly explain the central idea.

Symbiotic Relationships

Symbiosis is a third type of interaction among organisms. **Symbiosis** (sim bee OH sis) is any relationship in which two species live closely together. There are three types of symbiotic relationships: commensalism, mutualism, and parasitism. Just like predation and competition, symbiotic interactions, occur in all ecosystems. All organisms share patterns of interactions with their environments, both living and nonliving. An organism cannot survive without relying on another for survival.

Mutualism In some interactions, two species may depend on one another. In California's chaparral ecosystem, Harvester ants build their mounds near Indian Rice Grass. The ants attack any organism that comes to eat the grass. The Harvester ants depend on the Indian Rice Grass to get food. The grass depends on the ants for protection. This relationship is an example of **mutualism** (MYOO choo uh liz um), which is a relationship in which both species benefit. Some mutually beneficial interactions can become so **interdependent** that each organism requires the other for survival.

Commensalism Birds build nests in trees to make a place to live. The tree is unharmed. This relationship is an example of **commensalism**. Commensalism (kuh MEN suh liz um) is a relationship in which one species benefits and the other species is neither helped nor harmed.

Commensalism is not very common in nature because two species are usually either helped or harmed a little by any interaction. Scientists may disagree on whether a particular relationship truly demonstrates commensalism.

Identifying examples of commensalism can be difficult. For example, sea otters wrap themselves in kelp in order to anchor themselves while they sleep. Because the kelp is not affected, this species interaction could be an example of commensalism. On the other hand, sea otters also eat sea urchins which eat kelp thus limiting their growth. Kelp forests with sea otters can grow as high as 250 feet, making it an example of mutualism. When kelp grows to its maximum height, it gets better access to sunlight, an important abiotic factor for their survival. **Figure 5** shows more examples of symbiotic relationships across multiple ecosystems.

Mutualism and Commensalism

Figure 5 Some relationships more clearly show benefits to one or both species than others.

1. Synthesize Information ✎ Read each image caption. Label each photo "M" for mutualism or "C" for commensalism in the circle provided.
2. SEP Cite Evidence ✎ Beneath each image, use evidence to justify how you classified the relationship.

Hummingbirds feed on nectar deep within a flower. While sipping, the flower's pollen rubs off on the hummingbird. The bird can carry it to another flower.

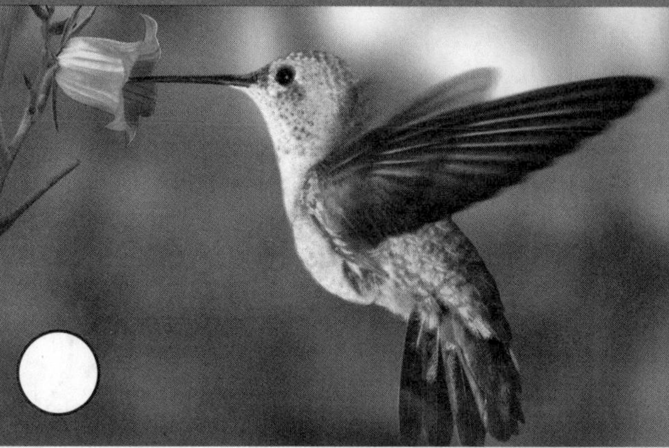

SEP Evidence ....

....

....

The banded mongoose feeds on ticks and other tiny animals that nestle in the warthog's fur and feed off of the warthog.

SEP Evidence ....

....

....

....

Barnacles feed by filtering tiny organisms from the water. They grow on objects below the surface, such as piers and rocks, and attach themselves to whales.

SEP Evidence ....

....

....

....

Remora attach themselves to the underside of a manta ray with a suction-cup-like structure. Mantas are messy eaters and remora feed on the food scraps.

SEP Evidence ....

....

....

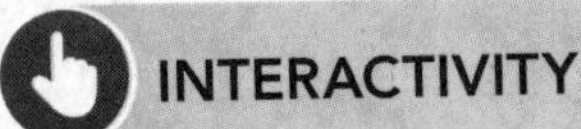

Interpret models of relationships in different ecosystems.

Parasitism If you've ever seen a dog continually scratching itself, then it may have fleas. This interaction is an example of **parasitism** (PAHR uh sit iz um). Parasitism is a relationship that involves one organism living with, on, or inside another organism and harming it.

The organism that benefits is called a parasite. The host is the organism that the parasite lives in or on. The parasite is generally smaller than its host. The fleas, for example, are parasites that harm the dog by biting it to feed on its blood for nourishment. Pets can suffer from severe health problems as a result of these bites. Study the examples of parasitism in **Figure 6**.

Parasitic Relationships

Figure 6 Unlike a predator, a parasite does not usually kill the organism it feeds on. If the host dies, the parasite could lose its source of food or shelter.

CHECK POINT **Integrate with Visuals** In each picture, label the host and the parasite shown.

SEP Construct Explanations How does parasitism differ from other symbiotic relationships?

....

....

....

....

....

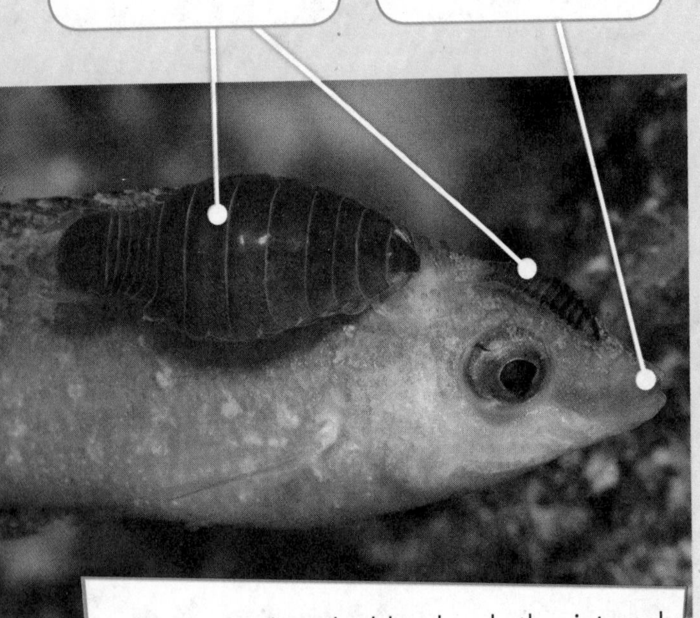

Fish lice feed on the blood and other internal fluids of the fish. Eventually the fish may quit eating and lose color from the stress caused by the lice.

A braconid wasp lays its eggs under the skin of the hornworm, a common pest in California gardens. As the larvae develop, they feed on the insides of the hornworm. Once fully developed, the larvae emerge and spin silk cocoons on the hornworm.

LESSON 1 Check

MS-LS2-1, MS-LS2-2, EP&CIIb

1. **Identify** What are the five different types of interactions between organisms?

Use the graph you constructed on wolf and moose populations to help you answer Questions 2 and 3.

2. **CCC Patterns** What patterns do scientists observe between predator-prey relationships like the wolves and moose on Isle Royale?

3. **SEP Interpret Data** Use the data from your graph to provide evidence for the effects of resource availability on individuals and populations in an ecosystem.

4. **SEP Construct Explanations** Do the patterns of interactions between organisms, such as competition and predation, change when they occur in different ecosystems? Explain.

5. **CCC Cause and Effect** Predict the effects on a predator-prey relationship, such as the one between a frog and blue heron, in a wetland ecosystem in the midst of a drought.

Quest CHECK-IN

In this lesson, you learned how organisms in ecosystems interact with one another and how resource availability can affect these interactions. You also discovered that these interactions can influence population size.

CCC Analyze Systems Why is it important to maintain existing organism interactions and availability of resources when building a new highway?

INTERACTIVITY

Research Animal Crossings

Go online to investigate the effects of highways and animals crossings.

Dynamic and Resilient Ecosystems

HANDS-ON LAB

uInvestigate Identify examples of succession in a local ecosystem.

MS-LS2-1 Analyze and interpret data to provide evidence for the effects of resource availability on organisms and populations of organisms in an ecosystem.

MS-LS2-2 Construct an explanation that predicts patterns of interactions among organisms across multiple ecosystems.

MS-LS2-4 Construct an argument supported by empirical evidence that changes to physical or biological components of an ecosystem affect populations.

(Also **EP&CIIb, EP&CIIIa, EP&CIIIb, EP&CIIIc**)

Connect It!

Circle the living organisms in the photo. Think about why the number of living organisms is limited here.

Predict How do you think this landscape will change in the future?

....

....

Succession

Ecosystems and their communities are dynamic in nature. They are always changing, because their characteristics can vary over time. Natural disasters, such as floods and tornadoes, can cause rapid change. Other changes occur over centuries or even longer. Humans can have a major impact on ecosystems as well. The series of predictable changes that occur in a community over time is called **succession**. **Figure 1** shows how organisms can establish habitats in even the harshest environments.

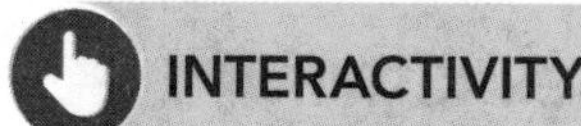

INTERACTIVITY

Consider what happens when an ecosystem is disturbed.

Primary Succession Disruptions to the physical or biological components of an ecosystem can impact organism populations living there. For example, lava from a volcanic eruption is creating new land by the sea. When the lava cools and hardens, no organisms are present. Over time, living things will **colonize** these areas. Primary succession is the series of changes that occur in an area where no soil or organisms exist.

Academic Vocabulary

Where else have you heard the term *colonize*, or the related term *colony*? Provide an example.

....

....

....

....

Pioneer Species The first species to populate an area are called **pioneer species.** These species are usually mosses and lichens, carried to the area by wind or water. Lichens are fungi and algae growing in a symbiotic relationship. They give off acidic compounds that help dissolve rock into soil. As pioneer species die, their remains add nutrients to the thin soil and help build it up.

Succession

Figure 1 Harsh landscapes like this hardened lava flow transform over time as lichens and plants establish themselves.

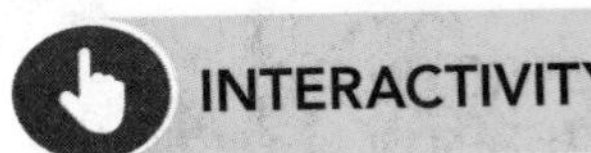

INTERACTIVITY

Investigate how ecosystems can change over time.

Literacy Connection

Write Arguments
Write a letter to a local government official explaining the importance of preventing disruptions to mature communities. In your letter, include evidence to support your claim.

Mature Communities Small changes in one part of a system can cause large changes in another part. For example, because lichens help to form a thin layer of soil, seed-producing plants can then establish themselves. Wind, water, and birds can bring seeds into the area. If the soil is adequate and there's enough rainfall, seedlings will emerge and may grow to adulthood. As the plants grow, they will shed leaves that will break down to make more soil. Plants also attract animals that will further enhance the soil by leaving waste and their own remains. Over time, the buildup of organic matter will improve the soil and allow for a more diverse community to establish itself in the area.

Succession demonstrates how all natural systems go through cycles and processes that are required for their functioning. While it can take centuries for a community to mature, once a community is established it can last for thousands of years or more if it is not disturbed or disrupted.

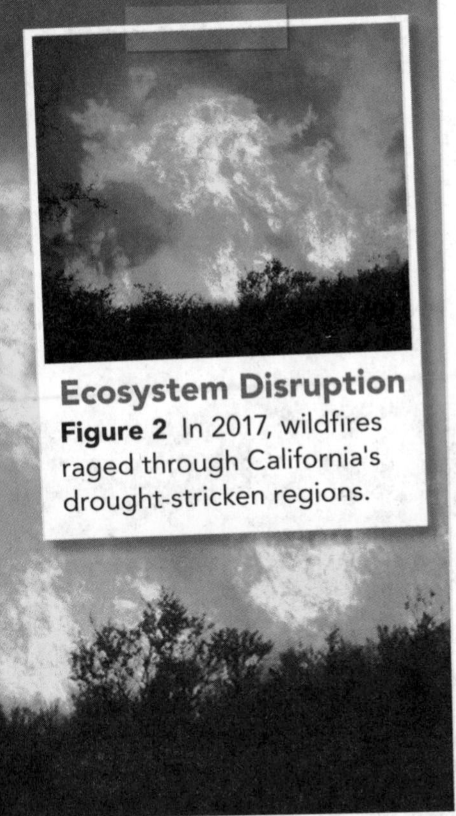

Ecosystem Disruption
Figure 2 In 2017, wildfires raged through California's drought-stricken regions.

Secondary Succession Devastating fires, such as the one shown in **Figure 2**, can result from natural system processes or human activities. Regardless of their cause, fires lead to secondary succession. Secondary succession is the series of changes that occur in an area where the ecosystem has been disturbed, but where soil and organisms already exist. Natural disruptions that affect the physical and biological components of an ecosystem include fires, hurricanes, tsunamis, and tornadoes. Human activities may also disturb an ecosystem and cause secondary succession to occur.

Unlike primary succession (**Figure 3**), secondary succession occurs in a place where an ecosystem and community exist. Secondary succession usually occurs more rapidly than primary succession because soil is already present and seeds from some plants may remain in the soil. Over time, more and more organisms can live in the area and it starts to resemble places that were never disturbed in the first place.

Empirical evidence is what's based on experience or verified by observation. Scientists follow common rules for obtaining and evaluating empirical evidence. What we know about succession in natural ecosystems is based on both empirical evidence and on data that has been gathered and analyzed over years and even decades.

CHECK POINT **Cite Textual Evidence** How is secondary succession different from primary succession?

....

....

....

Model It!

Pioneers

Figure 3 The images show how pioneer species begin the process of succession, which changes an area over time.

Integrate Information Draw pictures to represent the missing stages of primary succession.

2

4

1. **Claim** Identify a place in your community where succession might occur if people abandoned the area.

2. **Evidence** Describe what the location would look like years later after being abandoned.

3. **Reasoning** Explain how changes to the physical and biological components of the ecosystem would affect the populations that make up the community.

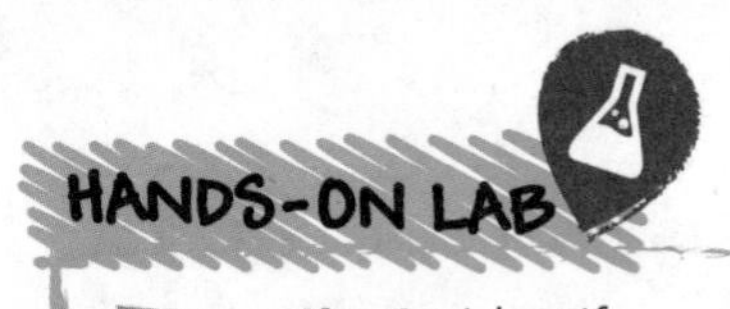

Investigate Identify examples of succession in a local ecosystem.

INTERACTIVITY

Propose causes for a change in a population and predict future changes.

Academic Vocabulary

What does it mean when a sports team *dominates* its rival team?

....

....

....

Ecosystem Disruptions and Population Survival

Disruptions to any physical or biological component of an ecosystem can lead to shifts in all its populations. When changes occur suddenly or last for a long time, most populations in the ecosystem do not survive. However, some organisms do survive the changes. Organisms surviving a fast-changing ecosystem often have adaptations that help them thrive in the new conditions.

Georgia, South Carolina, and Florida have an ecosystem of the longleaf pine forest, as shown in **Figure 4.** Longleaf pine trees **dominate** this ecosystem. These trees grow in a pattern that permits sunlight to reach the forest floor. Longleaf pine seeds need a soil free from undergrowth and germinate quickly in the soil. Longleaf pines are dependent on regular forest fires from lightning strikes to burn away grasses and invasive hardwood trees such as oak to remain healthy and reproduce. Mature trees' bark and early growth are fire-resistant.

Longleaf pines support a healthy ecosystem. Red-cockaded woodpeckers depend on mature trees for nesting sites. If fires don't burn the undergrowth, predators can reach the nests. Swallowed-tailed kites build nests high in the trees. Bachmann's sparrows favor mature pine forests where underbrush has been removed by fires. These bird populations have been reduced due to logging of the longleaf pines and previous fire suppression practices, which opened space for invasive oaks.

Most organisms reappear at some point after the fire because of adaptations such as heat-resistant seeds that may sprout or underground roots that can grow. Young longleaf pines develop a long taproot that enables them to grow after a fire.

Changes to Populations

Figure 4 In the longleaf pine ecosystem, some organisms are adapted to survive fire and others are not.

CHECK POINT **Determine Central Ideas** How does a wildfire impact a population of oak trees?

....

....

CCC Cause and Effect How might a wildfire help the longleaf pine population survive a deadly fungal infection on the needles of seedlings?

....

....

The red-cockaded woodpecker flies away from the fire to safety.
As the thick, scaly bark burns, flakes fall off and take the heat with them.
A longleaf pine seedling is topped with a moist tuft of needles. As fire burns the needles, they produce steam that moves the heat away from the plant and extinguishes the fire. If the needles burn off entirely, the seedling can regrow from its root.
Fire burns the blades of bluestem grass, but its underground roots remain unharmed. After the fire, new shoots sprout from the roots.
The pine snake escapes fire by seeking shelter in a gopher burrow.

LESSON 2 Check

MS-LS2-1, MS-LS2-2, MS-LS2-4, EP&CIIb, EP&CIIIa, EP&CIIIb, EP&CIIIc

1. **SEP Construct Explanations** What are pioneer species? How do they affect the variety of organisms in an ecosystem?

2. **SEP Engage in Argument** Support the argument that a forest fire impacts a population of birds that nest in the trees.

3. **Connect to Environmental Principles and Concepts** Explain how the physical and biological components of this ecosystem in Chico, California, are being disrupted.

Quest CHECK-IN

In this lesson you learned that changes to physical or biological components of an ecosystem can affect the populations of organisms that live there.

Apply Concepts How might mature communities of organisms be affected by the construction of a new highway? How does an animal crossing solve some of these problems?

INTERACTIVITY

Community Opinions

Go online to learn about reactions to a proposed crossing from members of the community. Based on the feedback, consider the constraints the animal crossing should meet.

"A Bird came down the Walk"

Emily Dickinson

A Bird came down the Walk—
He did not know I saw—
He bit an Angle Worm in halves
And ate the fellow, raw.

And then, he drank a Dew
From a convenient Grass—
And then hopped sidewise to the Wall
To let a Beetle pass—

He glanced with rapid eyes
That hurried all abroad—
They looked like frightened Beads, I thought—
He stirred his Velvet Head.—

Like one in danger, Cautious,
I offered him a Crumb,
And he unrolled his feathers,
And rowed him softer home—

Than Oars divide the Ocean,
Too silver for a seam,
Or Butterflies, off Banks of Noon,
Leap, plashless as they swim.

CONNECT TO YOU

With a classmate, discuss what you think the poem is about. How is the speaker in the poem similar to a scientist?

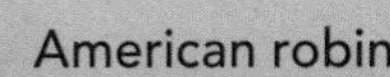

American robin

LESSON

3 Biodiversity

HANDS-ON LAB

uInvestigate Explore the role of keystone species in maintaining biodiversity.

MS-LS2-4 Construct an argument supported by empirical evidence that changes to physical or biological components of an ecosystem affect populations.

MS-LS2-5, Evaluate competing design solutions for maintaining biodiversity and ecosystem services. (Also **EP&CIc, EP&CIIb, EP&CIIIa, EP&CIIIb, EP&CIIIc, EP&CIVc, EP&CVa**)

Connect It!

Circle the parts of the ecosystem shown here that you think are important to people.

Identify Unknowns What do you think are two important ways that humans benefit from a healthy ecosystem? Explain.

....

....

The Value of Biodiversity

Earth is filled with many different ecosystems that provide habitats for each and every organism. Some organisms live in one ecosystem their entire lives. Other organisms are born in one ecosystem and migrate to another. Healthy ecosystems have biodiversity. The number and variety of different species in an area is **biodiversity**. Healthy ecosystems have biodiversity and also provide the opportunity for different species to interact. This is often essential for their survival, such as a predator finding prey.

Even small changes in an ecosystem's condition or available resources can produce larger changes that impact the entire ecosystem. Biodiversity increases as more resources are available. It decreases when fewer resources are available. When biodiversity changes, it impacts ecosystem processes. This impact may affect the health of an ecosystem.

Biodiversity also has both economic and ecological **value**. Healthy ecosystems, such as the one in **Figure 1**, provide resources and materials that we use. We consume food, fuel, medicines, and fibers from healthy ecosystems.

Academic Vocabulary

What does it mean when someone says that a person was raised with good values? Provide two examples.

....

....

....

....

....

Healthy Ecosystems

Figure 1 Biodiversity determines the health of an ecosystem.

Academic Vocabulary

How would you explain the term *economic* to someone who did not understand the meaning?

Economic Value

Humans use ecosystems for our own profit. There is value in using ecosystems to fulfill our basic needs and wants. The products we take from ecosystems have **economic** value, such as providing a household income. People can profit from healthy ecosystems both directly or indirectly.

Resources that are consumed from an ecosystem provide a direct value. For example, the crops from the vineyard in **Figure 2** are direct value. The farmer used the land and grew the crops to make a profit on their sale. In addition to food, medicines and raw materials provide resources and income. Unfortunately, demand for resources can harm biodiversity and ecosystems. Humans can use too many resources at once. As a result, many ecosystems do not have time to recover and are damaged. This can hurt humans in the long run.

Some resources in an ecosystem are used, but not consumed. These indirect values also affect the economic value. Shade trees reduce utility bills and provide wind protection. Wetlands reduce soil erosion, control flooding, and reduce large temperature swings. Hiking, touring unique habitats, and recreational activities provide revenue. The key is using these ecosystem resources for profit without destroying them.

Literacy Connection

Cite Textual Evidence As you read, underline the activities discussed in the text that support the claim that biodiversity has value. As with all claims, you can assess that the reasoning is sound by finding relevant and sufficient evidence in the text.

CHECK POINT **Determine Central Ideas** What makes crops a direct value from an ecosystem?

Economic Loss

Figure 2 Disease and poor weather conditions can cause severe financial losses for farmers. This vineyard in Hopeland, California, flooded after historic rainstorms.

SEP Construct Explanations Would it be wise for a farmer to grow just one type of crop? Explain.

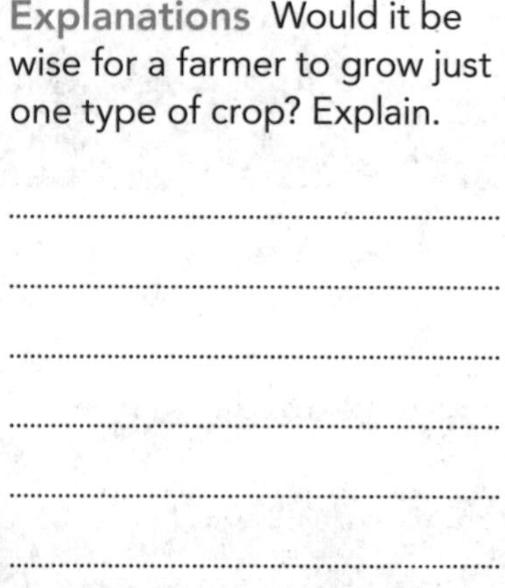

A Valuable Tree

Figure 3 Elephants eat the fruit of the balanite, or desert date, tree. The elephants then spread the seeds in their waste as they travel.

CCC Cause and Effect Consider the interdependence between the tree and the elephant. What would happen if one of the species were to decline in number?

....

....

Investigate Explore the role of keystone species in maintaining biodiversity.

Ecological Value All species function within an ecosystem. Each species performs a certain role. All species are connected and depend on each other for survival. A **keystone species** is a species that influences the survival of many other species in an ecosystem. One example of a keystone species is the African elephant.

African elephant herds appeared to be stripping vegetation from the ecosystem, thereby harming it. Some park officials wanted to control the elephant population by thinning the herds. Instead, they let the herds range freely. When the elephants uprooted trees, that made way for grasslands and smaller animals. Shrubs grew where the trees once stood and fed the animals unable to reach taller trees. Over time, the park ecosystem, **Figure 3**, returned to an ecological balance. Changes to physical and biological factors of an ecosystem, such as the number of elephants and trees, affect all of the populations within an ecosystem.

Biodiversity sustains ecosystems by protecting land and water resources, and aiding in nutrient cycling. Trees and vegetation hold soil in place to prevent erosion and landslides. Roots break up rocks to allow water to enter the soil. Animal waste sustains soil fertility. A diverse ecosystem is stable, productive, and can easily withstand environmental changes.

CHECK POINT **Summarize Text** Why is the elephant considered a keystone species?

....

....

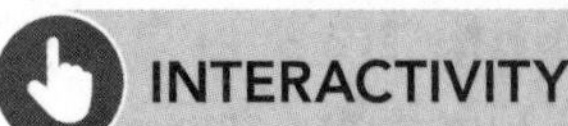

Explore the diversity of species that live in the Amazon.

Factors Affecting Biodiversity

There are numerous ecosystems on Earth. Biodiversity within these ecosystems varies from place to place. Various factors affect biodiversity, including niche diversity, genetic diversity, extinction, climate, and area.

Niche Diversity Every species in an ecosystem occupies a unique niche. The abiotic and biotic resources that a species needs to survive are provided by its niche. These resources include food, water, and habitat. The niches of different populations within an ecosystem interact with one another. Some species, like the panda in **Figure 4**, live in a narrow niche with only a few food sources. Species that have a narrow niche are more vulnerable to environmental changes. A niche can also be shared by two different species. When this happens, they compete for resources. If resources are low, one species may survive while the other must leave or die out. A healthy ecosystem reflects a balance among different populations and their unique niches.

A Narrow Niche

Figure 4 The panda's diet has no diversity. Its diet consists almost entirely of leaves, stems, and shoots from different bamboo species. Pandas can eat over 30 kg of bamboo a day. Circle the bamboo in the image.

CCC Analyze Systems What would happen to the panda population if there were a decrease in the amount of bamboo available? Explain.

....

....

....

....

....

....

Question It!

Endangered Species

Figure 5 Gray wolves are endangered. Scientists speculate that their near-extinction status could be due to low genetic diversity, loss of natural food resources, or loss of habitat.

SEP Ask Questions A group of scientists is visiting your school to discuss the importance of saving the gray wolf population. They need your help to design a solution to increase the number of gray wolves in California. However, you must first understand a little more about the endangered species. Each person is required to ask at least three questions of the experts. In the space below, write your questions. Consider constraints when developing your questions.

....

....

....

Genetic Diversity You may have heard the expression "gene pool." It is the number of genes available within a population. Genetic diversity, on the other hand, is the total number of inherited traits in the genetic makeup of an entire species. The greater its genetic diversity, the more likely it is that a species can adapt and survive. Species with low genetic diversity lack the ability to adapt to changing environmental conditions. The gray wolves you see in **Figure 5** could have low genetic diversity, which would contribute to their near-extinction status.

Species Extinction According to fossil evidence, about 99.9% of all species that have ever existed on Earth are now extinct. The disappearance of all members of a species from Earth is **extinction**. Species in danger of becoming extinct are endangered species. And species that could become endangered in the near future are threatened species. There are two ways in which species can become extinct. Background extinction occurs over a long period of time. It usually involves only one species. Environmental changes or the arrival of a competitor cause background extinctions. Mass extinction can kill many different species in a very short time. Mass extinctions are caused by rapid climate changes (such as from a meteoroid impact), continuous volcanic eruptions, or changes in the air or water.

CHECK POINT **Summarize Text** Why are populations with low genetic diversity, like gray wolves, less likely to survive?

....

....

Other Factors The climate and size of an ecosystem also affect biodiversity. Scientists hypothesize that a consistent climate supports biodiversity. One of the most diverse places on Earth is the tropical rainforest. Temperatures do not fluctuate greatly and it receives a large amount of rainfall. Also, plants grow year-round, providing food for animals. An ecosystem's area, or the amount of space that an ecosystem covers, also determines its biodiversity. For example, more species are found in an ecosystem that covers 50 square kilometers, than in one that covers 10 square kilometers. An ecosystem with a larger area will generally have more biodiversity.

Math Toolbox

Room to Roam

A savanna is a grassland ecosystem with few trees. About 65 percent of Africa is covered by savannas. Lions roam where there are fewer than 25 people per square mile. As the human population in Africa increases, the amount of land where lions roam is decreasing. Use the chart and graphs to answer the questions.

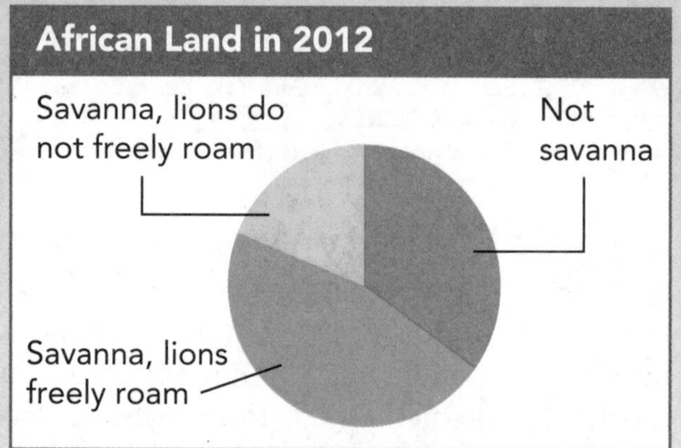

1. **Predict** Describe how the green area of the pie chart would change to show the area where lions freely roam today.

2. **Draw Conclusions** How has the balance in the African lion population shifted over time? What caused this shift?

3. **Use Ratio Reasoning** Write a ratio comparing the lion population in 1950 to 2000. Explain the relationship between human population and the lion population.

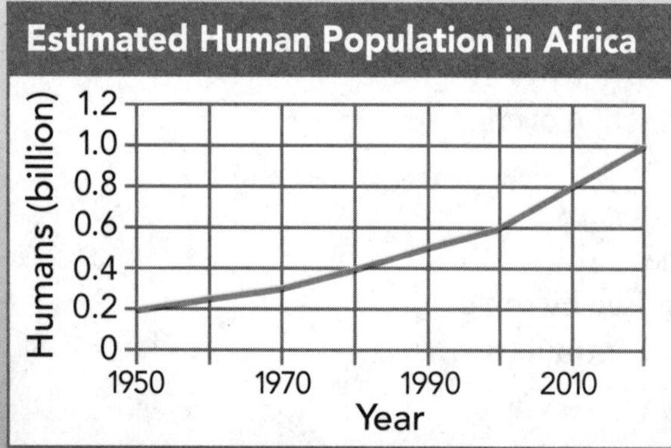

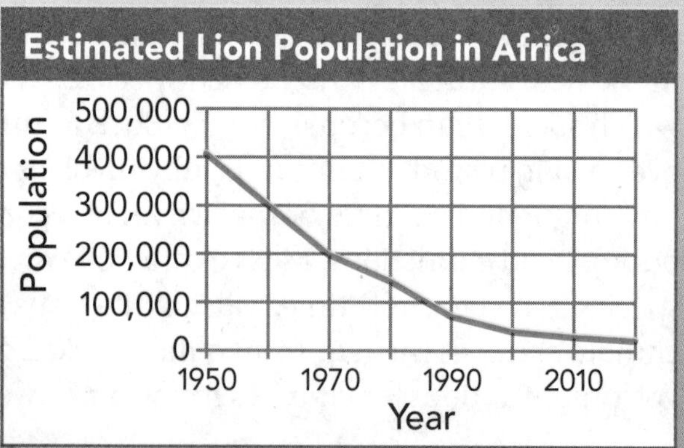

Human Impact

When an ecosystem is harmed in any way, its biodiversity is reduced. Human activities directly impact ecosystems and the organisms that live there. As you see in **Figure 6**, human activities can impact the environment.

Our Impact on Ecosystems

Figure 6 For each image, determine if the human activities are increasing or decreasing impacts on the environment. Place an "I" in the circle for an increased impact, and a "D" in the circle for a decreased impact. Then, in the space provided, provide evidence to support your determination.

Threats to Coral

Figure 7 ✏ These images show two different coral reef ecosystems. One image shows how an increase in water temperature can harm a coral reef through coral bleaching. When water gets too warm, coral can become stressed, causing the algae living in their tissue to leave. Because the coral relies on algae for food, it begins to starve. Circle the image that shows coral bleaching.

CHECK POINT

Determine Conclusions What evidence is presented to show that a warming climate can impact biodiversity?

....

....

....

....

....

....

....

Damaging Biodiversity Human activities cause most of the harm to habitats and ecosystems. The result is a loss of biodiversity. For example, removing natural resources from an ecosystem can reduce its biodiversity.

Scientists agree that increased levels of carbon dioxide gas contribute to climate change. One way humans contribute to climate change is by the removal of resources from ecosystems. For example, people remove trees for farming, houses, and timber. The use of machinery to remove and process the trees increases the amount of carbon dioxide gas in our atmosphere. In addition, the deforested plants are not taking in carbon dioxide. Changes to the climate impact all of Earth's ecosystems. It is easy to observe changes in temperature on land, but ocean water temperature also changes. **Figure 7** shows how a changing climate threatens biodiversity.

Human activities can also introduce non-native species, called **invasive species**, into a habitat. Often, invasive species out-compete native species within an ecosystem. Humans also remove species when poachers illegally kill wildlife for clothing, medicine, or body parts such as horns for ivory.

Protecting Biodiversity We can all take action to protect wildlife on Earth. For example, **Figure 8** shows students collecting data for conservation projects. Captive breeding programs help endangered species reproduce and sustain diversity. States and countries can set aside land to safeguard natural habitats. Finally, international laws and treaties protect the environment and biodiversity.

Habitat Preservation The goal of habitat preservation is to maintain the natural state of an ecosystem. Sometimes, that requires restoring its biodiversity. National parks, marine fisheries, and wildlife refuges are areas that preserve habitats. These areas are wildlife sanctuaries. Laws prevent or severely restrict any removal of resources from wildlife sanctuaries.

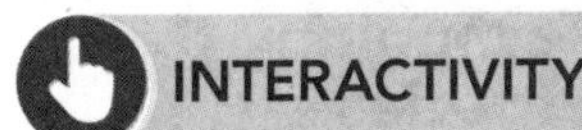

INTERACTIVITY

Examine how humans can safeguard and preserve biodiversity.

Student Discourse
With a partner, discuss what you value about being out in nature. Consider the number and variety of species you see there. What would happen if some of them disappeared?

Citizen Scientists

Figure 8 Scientists often seek help from people like you for preservation and conservation efforts. Citizens are trained to collect data on factors such as water quality, population numbers, and behavior of species. Scientists use the data to track populations and to monitor preservation efforts.

SEP Engage in Argument Do you think citizen volunteers should participate in citizen science projects? Explain.

....

....

....

....

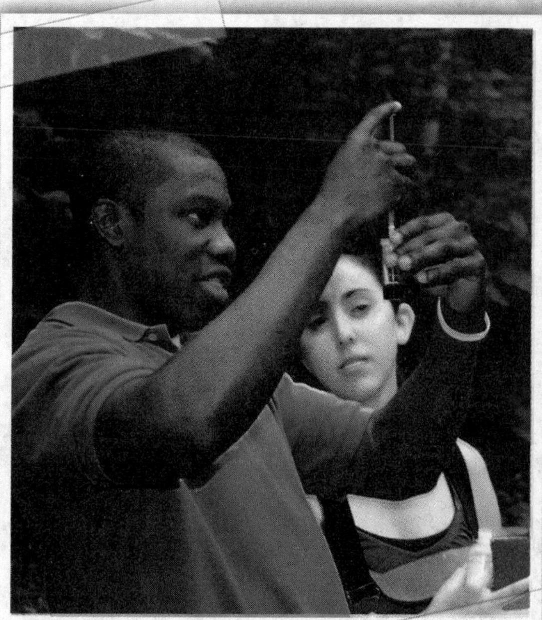

Using Technology to Save a Species

Figure 9 Innovations in technology, such as cameras with artificial intelligence, let people learn about endangered marine species, like this vaquita. With that knowledge comes the desire to protect them.

Global Cooperation Habitat preservation is the most important way to protect the existing species on our planet. Two treaties are dedicated to preserving global biodiversity. The Convention on Biological Diversity focuses on conservation. The Convention on International Trade in Endangered Species of Wild Fauna and Flora ensures that the trade of plants and animals does not endanger them. These two treaties protect over 30,000 plant and animal species. We all benefit from global efforts that protect Earth's biodiversity. Protection and conservation ensure resources for future generations (**Figure 10**).

Technology and engineering play a key role in species conservation. Researchers at the University of California in San Diego have combined robotics and camera vision to track and study the rare and endangered vaquita (**Figure 9**), also known as the Gulf of California harbor porpoise.

Protecting Our Oceans

Figure 10 The Sea of Cortez is a protected marine ecosystem. It's also where the world's remaining one hundred vaquitas live in the wild today. Global support for protecting Earth's marine ecosystems is increasing. Circle two organisms that could be harmed without marine protection.

CHECK POINT **Determine Conclusions** Why is it important to protect marine ecosystems?

....

....

....

LESSON 3 Check

MS-LS2-4, MS-LS2-5, EP&CIc, EP&CIIb, EP&CIIIa, EP&CIIIb, EP&CIIIc, EP&CIVc, EP&CVa

1. **SEP Construct Explanations** What is meant by the value of biodiversity?

2. **Distinguish Relationships** How is an ecosystem's biodiversity a measure of its health?

3. **CCC Cause and Effect** What consequences might occur if a particular species becomes extinct?

4. **Connect to Environmental Principles and Concepts** Support the argument that humans must take measures to protect biodiversity. Explain.

Quest CHECK-IN

In this lesson, you learned about the value of healthy ecosystems and the importance of biodiversity. You also learned about the factors affecting biodiversity.

Synthesize Information How can road construction affect the biodiversity of an ecosystem?

HANDS-ON LAB

Design and Model a Crossing

Go online for a downloadable worksheet of this lab. Build a model of your wildlife crossing. As a class, share your ideas. Evaluate how each model functions to protect biodiversity.

LESSON 4

Ecosystem Services

HANDS-ON LAB

uInvestigate Model how wetlands help with water purification.

MS-LS2-3 Develop a model to describe the cycling of matter and flow of energy among living and nonliving parts of an ecosystem.

MS-LS2-5 Evaluate competing design solutions for maintaining biodiversity and ecosystem services. (Also **EP&CIc**, **EP&CIIIa**, **EP&CIIIb**, **EP&CIIIc**, **EP&CIVc**, **EP&CVa**)

Connect It!

Circle three different organisms interacting with their environment.

Distinguish Relationships Describe how each organism interacts with the environment. How would they be affected if the environment was disrupted?

Ecosystem Services

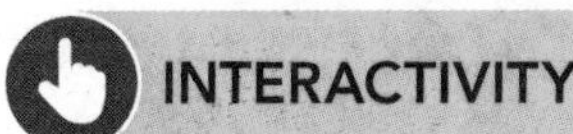

Explore the services provided by a healthy ecosystem.

Ecosystems meet our needs by supplying us with water, fuel, and wellness. **Ecosystem services** are the benefits humans receive from ecosystems. They are often produced without help from humans, and they are free! Ecosystem services occur because systems in an ecosystem interact with one another. Plants interact with the air, sun, soil, water, and minerals. Animals interact with plants, other animals, the air, and water. Because services are exchanged when interactions occur, biodiversity is an important factor.

In an ecosystem, all organisms, including humans, interact with one another and benefit from those interactions. **Ecology** is the study of how organisms interact with their environment. Ecology helps us understand how services emerge from those interactions. For example, the bee in **Figure 1** is pollinating the flower, but it is also getting nectar from the flower. Both interactions can result in services that humans use. Further, their exchange is an example of cycling matter and energy within an ecosystem.

Humans rely on cycling of matter and energy that occurs in diverse ecosystems. Scientists have separated ecosystem services into four categories, based on how they benefit us. The categories are: cultural, provisional, regulatory, and supporting services. Identifying and protecting each service is vital for human life.

Ecosystem Services

Figure 1 Organisms interact with and rely on one another. This bee pollinates the flower, which will turn into a strawberry. Consider some benefits you might get from this ecosystem. Some of these benefits might be obvious, while others may not be.

Cultural Services Nature has a way of putting a smile on your face. When nature makes you happy, it is providing you with a cultural service. Cultural services include recreational services, such as paddling a canoe at a local lake or going on a hike, and educational services, such as exploring Earth's history in the rock layers. We use cultural services to rest and relax, or learn more about the world around us. We can even learn about history, such as the role of the Mississippi and Missouri Rivers in building our nation. **Figure 2** shows a few examples of the cultural services that give meaning to life and help our wellness.

Provisional Services *Provisional* means useful. Provisional services, also shown in **Figure 2**, are the products obtained from the natural resources in an ecosystem. Anything naturally occurring in the environment that humans use is a **natural resource**, such as drinking water, food, fuel, and raw materials. Filtered ground water and surface water are two sources we tap into for drinking water. Farming provides many of the meats, vegetables, and fruits we eat. Marine and freshwater ecosystems provide us with meat and vegetables. Fuel resources include oil, coal, and natural gas. Plants provide us with timber for buildings and plant-based medicines.

Cultural and Provisional Services

Figure 2 Cultural services make us feel well, while provisional services provide us with something to use. Circle any photo that shows a provisional service.

SEP Provide Evidence Which services, cultural or provisional, do humans pay the most money for? Explain.

Restoring Water

The water flowing into New York Harbor is polluted due to waste and fertilizer runoff. Scientists have designed a solution that relies on natural filtration and purification. One oyster filters about 150 liters of water a day, while one mussel filters 65 liters a day.

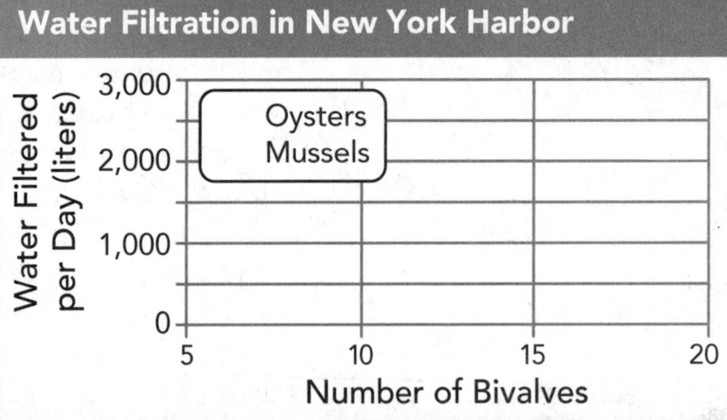

1. **Write an Expression** Write a formula to show the amount of water filtered by 7 oysters in one day.

....

....

2. **Graph Proportional Relationships** Use your formula to calculate the amount of water 5, 10, 15, and 20 oysters can filter. Then, calculate the amount of water the same number of mussels can filter. Graph your data. Use a solid line to represent the oysters and a dashed line to represent the mussels.

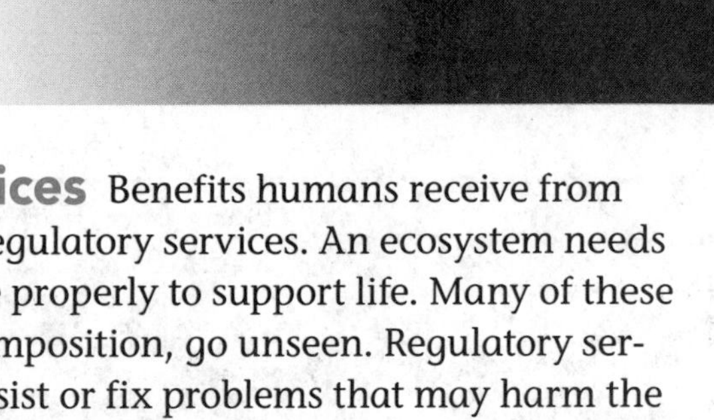

Regulatory Services Benefits humans receive from natural processes are regulatory services. An ecosystem needs to function and operate properly to support life. Many of these processes, such as decomposition, go unseen. Regulatory services allow nature to resist or fix problems that may harm the ecosystem. These processes also protect humans from some of the same problems.

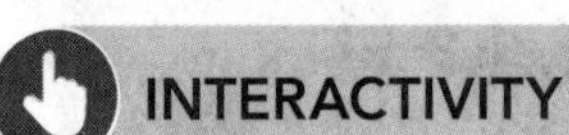

Test and evaluate competing solutions for preventing soil erosion to protect cropland.

Plants and animals play a major role in the regulation of an ecosystem. Plants increase air quality by removing harmful chemicals and releasing useful chemicals. They regulate our climate by absorbing a greenhouse gas—carbon dioxide. The roots of plants prevent soil erosion. Bivalves, such as mussels and oysters, filter polluted and contaminated water. We have fruits to eat because animals pollinate flowers and help disperse seeds. Some animals naturally help with pest and disease control. This natural regulation of pests is biological control.

CHECK POINT **Cite Textual Evidence** How are regulatory services important for ecosystems?

....

....

INTERACTIVITY

Explore the four key ecosystem services.

Supporting Services The most important ecosystem services are the ones that support all the processes in nature. While supporting services do not directly impact humans, ecosystems would cease to function without them.

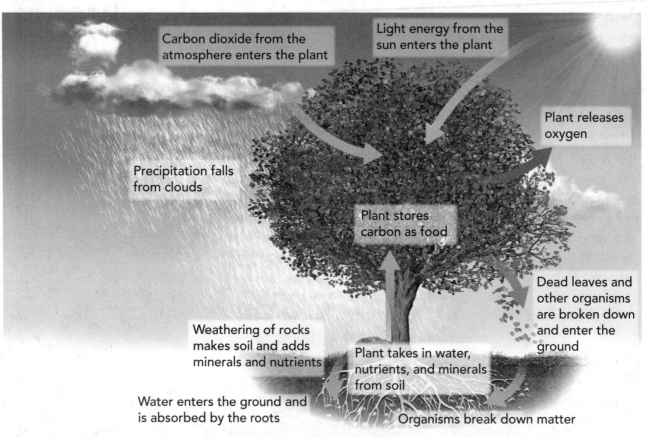

Supporting services cycle resources such as water, nutrients, gases, and soil throughout the ecosystem. In the water cycle, water evaporates, travels into the air and forms a part of a cloud, returns to Earth as precipitation, and the cycle continues. When an organism dies, it decomposes and forms nutrient-rich matter that becomes part of the soil. Plants take in the nutrients and store them in their cells. Atmospheric gases also cycle through ecosystems. During photosynthesis, plants take in carbon dioxide and release oxygen. Animals then take in oxygen and release carbon dioxide. Soil is also cycled. It is formed from weathered rock and organic matter. Rock sediment can reform into another rock with added heat and/or pressure. **Figure 3** shows how these different cycles interact with one another. The cycles ensure that matter and energy are endlessly transferred within a healthy ecosystem.

CHECK POINT **Determine Central Ideas** Why are supporting services important to the ecosystem?

....

....

Interactions Between Cycles of an Ecosystem

Figure 3 Draw two arrows to show the flow of water in this ecosystem.

Explain Phenomena What would happen if any of these services were disrupted?

....

....

....

Carbon dioxide from the atmosphere enters the plant
Light energy from the sun enters the plant
Plant releases oxygen
Precipitation falls from clouds
Plant stores carbon as food
Dead leaves and other organisms are broken down and enter the ground
Weathering of rocks makes soil and adds minerals and nutrients
Plant takes in water, nutrients, and minerals from soil
Water enters the ground and is absorbed by the roots
Organisms break down matter

Biodiversity in Ecosystems
Figure 4 The survival of marine ecosystems, like this coral reef, is dependent on the diversity of organisms. Coral reefs provide every type of ecosystem service. But sometimes those services can be in conflict. People who snorkel and scuba dive can damage the corals. Boats can increase water pollution. People can also overfish the area.

Specify Design Constraints Think about ways to preserve this ecosystem. What sort of management plan could maintain the ecosystem services a coral reef provides, while protecting it from the negative impact of human activities?

Factors Impacting Ecosystem Services

Earth needs diverse and healthy ecosystems. All organisms depend on their environment to get food, water, and shelter. Diverse ecosystems provide these basic needs for life.

Biodiversity Ecosystem production increases with biodiversity. When production increases, ecosystem services increase. Coral reefs, such as the one in **Figure 4**, cover less than one percent of the ocean. However, over 25 percent of the marine life lives among coral reefs. Each species plays a role within the ecosystem and they benefit from one another. Small fish eat algae, so the coral do not compete for resources with algae. Predators, such as sharks, keep the number of small fish from getting too large. Some fish eat parasites growing on other fish. Organisms like crabs feed on dead organisms.

As you can see, there are many more examples of biodiversity found at coral reefs. This biodiversity helps coral reefs survive changing conditions. However, coral reefs are increasingly threatened by our demand for their resources.

Avocado Farms

Figure 5 Avocado farmers in Mexico did not know that the roots of the native trees filter water. Avocado tree roots are not able to filter the ground water.

CCC Identify Patterns How has this impacted people who rely on naturally filtered drinking water?

HANDS-ON LAB

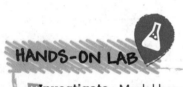

Investigate Model how wetlands help with water purification.

Human Activities When humans alter or destroy habitats, the natural cycling of the ecosystem is disrupted. The severe impact of human activities is mostly due to our ignorance and greed. Removing species from ecosystems disrupts natural cycling, which decreases ecosystem services. However, many people are working to restore and protect the natural cycling of ecosystems.

Scientific knowledge might be able to describe the environmental consequences of our actions, but it does not determine or recommend the decisions that we take as a society. For example, we once thought that our oceans could handle anything we dumped in them, from sewage to nuclear waste. We also assumed that the ocean was an endless supply of goods. Now we know that by polluting our oceans, we have lost marine organisms. By overfishing the Atlantic cod, bluefin tuna, and Chilean sea bass, we have caused their populations to decline drastically.

Changing the ecosystem impacts humans because it reduces the ecosystem services we rely on. The development of cities and demand for food further harms ecosystems. When buildings replace wetlands and floodplains, flooding and loss of biodiversity often result. To grow crops, farmers strip the land of native plant species, decreasing biodiversity. In Mexico, this became a problem when avocado farmers cleared native oak and pine trees to grow avocado trees, as shown in **Figure 5**.

Literacy Connection

Write Arguments Use the Internet to conduct research on the clearing of forests to create farmland. Research two opposing sides of the issue. Select one side of the issue to support. Cite specific claims and relevant evidence to explain why you chose that side.

Conservation

Over the past 50 years, human activities have drastically changed Earth's ecosystems. Scientists and engineers are working to design solutions to help save Earth's ecosystems. One way is through **conservation**, or the practice of using less of a resource so that it can last longer. As concerned citizens, we can all participate in conservation to protect and restore Earth's ecosystems.

INTERACTIVITY

Investigate how biodiversity impacts ecosystem services.

Protection Healthy ecosystems need protection from the loss of resources. **Sustainability** is the ability of an ecosystem to maintain biodiversity and production indefinitely. Designating protected areas and regulating the amount of resources humans can take from an ecosystem are two main efforts to promote sustainability. The **regulation** of protected areas can be difficult to enforce without monitors.

Academic Vocabulary

Why is it important for the school to have regulations?

Restoration **Ecological restoration** is the practice of helping a degraded or destroyed ecosystem recover from damage. Some recovery efforts are easy, like planting native plants. Others are more difficult. For example, toxic chemical spills require bioremediation, a technique that uses microorganisms to breakdown pollutants. Restoring land to a more natural state, or land reclamation, also helps ecosystems (**Figure 6**).

CHECK POINT **Determine Central Ideas** Why do scientists prefer to use bioremediation to clean up chemical spills?

Design It!

Ecological Restoration

Figure 6 Restoring an ecosystem often takes several years and several regulations.

SEP Design Your Solution Construction of a shopping mall has caused the deterioration of a wetland area. A study conducted showed that runoff from paved areas is disrupting the existing wetland. Create a plan to present to local officials outlining criteria for restoring the remaining wetland.

LESSON 4 Check

MS-LS2-3, MS-LS2-5, EP&CIc, EP&CIIb, EP&CIIIa, EP&CIIIb, EP&CIIIc, EP&CIVc, EP&CVa

1. **Identify** What are the four categories of ecosystem services?

2. **SEP Provide Evidence** How do cultural services help humans?

3. **Distinguish Relationships** How are biodiversity and the cycling of matter related to maintaining ecosystem services?

4. **SEP Design Solutions** What are several ways that you could conserve water?

5. **Explain Phenomena** What are supporting services and why are they important to cultural, provisional, and regulatory services?

6. **CCC Evaluate Proportion** Using your data from the math toolbox, which bivalve is more efficient at filtering water? Provide support.

7. **Apply Concepts** What are some other organisms, aside from bivalves, that could be used to purify water? Explain the benefits of using this organism.

8. **Connect to Environmental Principles and Concepts** A giant factory farm uses large open lagoons to treat waste from the buildings where hogs are housed. The problem is that the lagoons smell awful and during rainstorms they are at risk of spilling into surrounding river systems. Design a solution that resolves the smell and water contamination risk, and allows the farm to continue to raise hogs.

uEngineer It! Sustainable Design STEM

littleBits

MS-LS2-4, MS-LS2-5, ETS1-1, EP&CIc, EP&CIVc, EP&CVa

FROM BULLDOZERS To Biomes

INTERACTIVITY

Explore how to maintain marine ecosystems.

Do you know how to transform an old clay pit into lush biomes? You engineer it! The Eden Project in Cornwall, England shows us how.

The Challenge: To renew and transform land after humans have damaged it.

Phenomenon A clay pit in Cornwall had been mined for over a hundred years to make fine china and was shutting down. Mining provides access to resources, but can damage ecosystems by removing vegetation and topsoil. Mining can threaten biodiversity by destroying or fragmenting habitats, and increasing erosion and pollution.

Eden Project planners chose the clay pit to build a giant greenhouse to showcase biodiversity and the relationship between plants, people and resources.

The greenhouse represents two biomes: the rain forest biome and the Mediterranean biome. These biomes contain over a million plants and more than 5,000 different species. By comparison, in the California Floristic Province, a Mediterranean-type climate, there are over 2,000 different native plant species. Visitors can learn how plants are adapted to different climates, how plants play a role in their daily lives, and how to use resources sustainably.

The top photo shows the clay pit that was transformed into the biome structures and lush vegetation of the Eden Project below.

DESIGN CHALLENGE

Can you build a model of a biome structure? Go to the Engineering Design Notebook to find out!

You have limited materials to work with: 30 toothpicks and 15 balls of clay

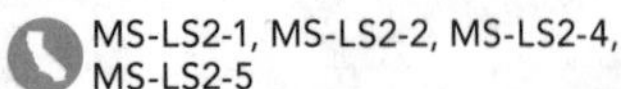

TOPIC 10 Review and Assess

MS-LS2-1, MS-LS2-2, MS-LS2-4, MS-LS2-5

Evidence-Based Assessment

Largemouth Bass (*Micropterus salmoides*) were introduced to the Sacramento-San Joaquin Delta in the 1890s. The species did not become common in the area until non-native Brazilian waterweed (*Egeria densa*), a submerged invasive aquatic plant, became abundant in the waterway around 1950. Brazilian waterweed forms a dense stand of vegetation. Largemouth Bass is now so common that in some areas of the Delta it is the most likely fish to be caught. Ecologists are concerned that this carnivorous fish might be eating native fish that have already declining populations. The delta is an area where freshwater meets salt water ocean, and so the Largemouth bass could potentially have an effect on the biodiversity of both fresh and saltwater species. It is home to many species protected both federally and by the California Endangered Species Act.

Researchers visited 33 sites every 2 months for two years. They caught Largemouth bass, emptied their stomachs and recorded what was inside. The stomachs of over 3,000 Largemouth Bass were sampled. A list of their stomach contents is summarized below.

Source: UC Davis 2019

Stomach contents in order of abundance	Examples	Percent of total diet (estimated)
Plankton	Amphipods	31–37
non-native crayfish	Red Swamp crayfish	20–38.8
Insect larvae	Fly, dragonfly, damselfly, true bugs	8.9–18.4
Other carnivorous fish	Non-native sunfish	0.6–21.1
Largemouth Bass	Small members of its own species	0–4.8
Native bottom dwelling fish	Prickly Sculpin	1.3–4.2
Non-bottom dwelling native fish	Pacific Lamprey, Tule Perch, Sacramento Blackfish, Hitch, Three-spined Stickleback	0.4–2.6
Pelagic Organism Decline (POD) Fish	Striped Bass, Threadfin shad, Delta Smelt, Longfin Smelt	<0.4

1. **CCC Cause and Effect** Why is it likely that the Largemouth Bass became more common after another introduced species, the Brazilian waterweed, also became more abundant?

2. **SEP Analyze Data** What is the best description of the relationship between Largemouth Bass and smaller members of the species?

   A. Competition
   B. Predator/Prey
   C. Mutualism
   D. Parasitism

3. **SEP Identify Patterns** Pelagic Organism Decline (POD) fish are both native (smelt) and non-native (bass and shad) open-ocean dwelling fish whose populations declined rapidly after the populations of carnivorous fish increased in the Delta. Does it appear that the diet of the Largemouth Bass is responsible for the POD trend? Explain.

4. **SEP Interpret Data** The population of the native Prickly Sculpin was found to increase in a study that was conducted from 1995 to 2015. What does that suggest, along with the data provided, about the effect of Largemouth Bass on native populations in this habitat?

5. **SEP Design Solutions** Ecologists are planning on dedicating more habitat to protect native species in the area and limit the populations of introduced species. Based on the information given about Largemouth Bass in the area, what habitat management method would you recommend to keep populations of Largemouth Bass low? Select all that apply.

   A. Prevent the spread of Brazilian waterweed in the newly protected habitat
   B. Stock the area with many smaller species of both native and nonnative fish
   C. Regularly monitor community populations of both fish and prey organisms
   D. Remove the POD species of fish from the new habitat to prevent luring Bass

uDemonstrate Lab

MS-LS2-1, MS-LS2-2, MS-LS2-3, MS-LS2-4, EP&CIIB, EP&CIIIa, EP&CIIIb, EP&CIIIc

Changes in an Ecosystem

How can you use a **model** to determine the effects of a **forest fire** on a **rabbit population**?

Background

Phenomenon Forest fires have a bad reputation! Many of these fires damage or destroy habitats and impact the populations of organisms that live there. But forest fires can also play an important role in maintaining the overall health of ecosystems. In this lab, you will develop and use a model to investigate how a forest fire might affect a population of rabbits 50 years after the fire.

Materials

(per group)

- tree-shadow circles handout
- scissors
- transparent tape

Young Longleaf Pine

Tree Shadow As Seen From Above

Mature Longleaf Pine

Tree Shadow As Seen From Above

Safety

Be sure to follow all safety guidelines provided by your teacher. The Safety Appendix of your textbook provides more details about the safety icons.

Oak Tree

Tree Shadow As Seen From Above

Procedure

- [ ] 1. Predict what will happen to the rabbit population 50 years after the fire. Will the population be smaller, the same size, or larger? Record your prediction.
- [ ] 2. The graph paper represents the forest floor where each square is equal to 10 square meters (m^2). Calculate the total area of the forest floor. Create a data table in the space provided and enter this area in the table.
- [ ] 3.  Cut out the tree shadow circles from the tree-shadow circles handout. Design a longleaf pine forest by arranging the mature pine and oak tree shadow circles on the forest floor. (Do not use the young pine tree shadows yet.) Tape the mature pine tree shadows in place, but not the oak tree shadows.
- [ ] 4. Determine the area of forest floor in sunlight. Add this data to your table.
- [ ] 5. Using a similar method, determine the square meters of shadow. Calculate the percentage of forest floor in shadow and in sunlight. Add this data to your table.
- [ ] 6. Suppose a lightning strike ignites a forest fire. Here's what would happen to some of the populations in the forest:
  - **Oak trees** are not adapted to survive fire so they burn and are destroyed; new trees will grow only if seeds are carried into the forest after the fire
  - **Longleaf pine trees** survive and continue to grow; seeds are released from pine cones and can germinate
  - **Bluestem grasses** are burned, but roots survive
- [ ] 7. Fast forward 50 years. The oak trees did not survive the forest fire, but the longleaf pines did. Use the young pine tree shadows to model the areas where young pine trees have likely grown. Repeat Steps 4 & 5 to gather evidence from your model about what the forest looks like 50 years after the fire.

HANDS-ON LAB

Demonstrate Go online for a downloadable worksheet of this lab.

uDemonstrate Lab

Prediction

Observations

Data Table

Analyze and Interpret Data

1. **Explain** What resources are the trees and grass competing for?

2. **SEP Analyze Data** Was your prediction correct? How did resource availability 50 years after the fire impact the rabbit population? (Hint: The rabbits are herbivores that primarily feed on grasses.)

3. **SEP Cite Evidence** Use the data you have collected as evidence to support the claim you made in Question 2.

4. **SEP Engage in Argument** Longleaf pine forests are important habitats, home to several endangered species. Oak trees are invasive (non-native) species in longleaf pine forests. When there are too many oak trees, they block the sunlight that pine trees need. Construct an argument that it is sometimes necessary to set forest fires in these habitats in order to preserve these endangered species.

Case Study

MS-LS2-2, MS-LS2-4, EP&CIIa, EP&CIIb, EP&CIIc, EP&CIVc, EP&CVa

The Dependable Elephant

The African elephant is the largest land mammal on Earth. It can grow to weigh more than 4,500 kilograms (10,000 pounds) and spend most of its days eating. This huge creature often lives in herds of 12 to 15 individuals that are led by a dominant female. An African elephant gives birth every 3 to 4 years, producing one calf after a two-year pregnancy. A calf can weigh about 110 kilograms (250 pounds) at birth.

Elephants serve an ecological role as big as their size. As a keystone species, they directly impact the structure, composition, and biodiversity of their ecosystem—where the vast grassy plains of the African savannas and woodlands meet. Elephants affect the variety and amount of trees that make up a forest. By pulling down trees and tearing up thorny bushes, they create grassland habitats for other species. Elephant dung enriches the soil with nutrients and carries the seeds of many plant species. In fact, some of the seeds need to pass through the elephant's digestive system to germinate! Other seeds are removed from the dung and eaten by other animals. Scientists estimate that at least one-third of Africa's woodlands depend on elephants for their survival in one way or another.

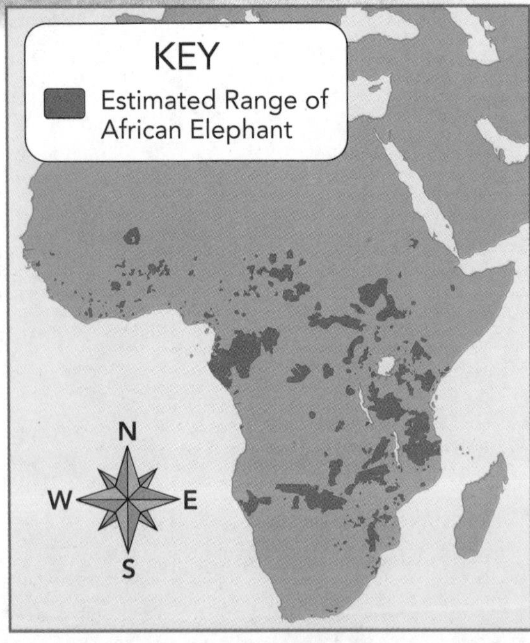

African elephants once numbered in the millions, but the numbers have been dropping. This dramatic decline is a result of poaching. Hunters kill the elephants for their ivory tusks. The valuable ivory is sold or used to make decorative items.

Saving the Elephants

Various elephant conservation groups suggest that there are scattered pockets of African elephants throughout the southern portions of the continent. While there are efforts being made to protect the elephants, there are just too few people and too much land to cover to be very effective.

The graph to the right shows the estimated African elephant population from 1995 through 2014. Use the graph to answer the questions.

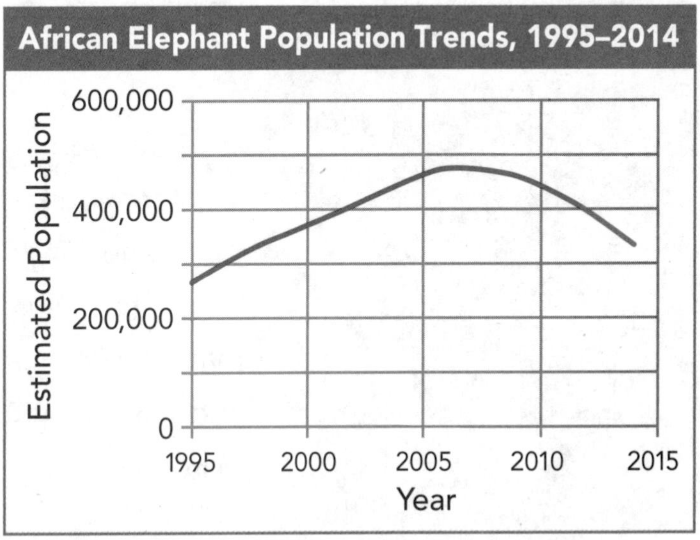

African Elephant Population Trends, 1995–2014

Source: Chase MJ, et. al. (2016) Continent-wide survey reveals massive decline in African savannah elephants. *PeerJ* 4:e2354

1. **CCC Patterns** Describe any patterns you see in the graph.

2. **Predict** Do you think the trend shown in the graph will continue? Explain.

3. **CCC Stability and Change** Based on the data, how might the rest of the elephant's ecosystem be affected long term?

4. **SEP Construct Explanations** What are some ways elephants could be protected in order to preserve the biodiversity of an ecosystem?

Case Study

MS-ESS2-5, MS-ESS3-2

THE CASE OF THE Runaway Hurricane

Have you ever lived through a hurricane? If so, you know how dangerous they can be. Hurricane winds range from 74 to nearly 200 miles per hour. Storm surges can be greater than 8 feet. These major storms can submerge whole neighborhoods and destroy houses.

During a hurricane, downed power lines result in widespread power outages, flooding can reach as high as the second floor of houses, and downed trees and telephone poles make roads dangerous or impassable. Roofs can be torn off buildings and hurled violently through the air, along with other movable property such as lawn chairs. The powerful storm can even cause some buildings to collapse.

Hurricanes generate far out at sea. They may pick up strength and speed over warm water as they move toward the coast, or weaken in cold water before they reach land. Florida's exceptionally long coastline and tropical location make it a prime target for hurricanes. These two factors explain why Florida is hit by more major hurricanes than any other U.S. state.

It doesn't take a direct hit to cause damage. In 2016, Hurricane Matthew did not hit Florida directly, but it dumped flooding rains on the state. Insurance claims for damage have thus far added up to more than $218 million.

There's no changing the fact that many states lie in the path of hurricanes. Officials in high-risk areas are working hard to find ways to lower the risks, including issuing new rules for storm-resistant structures and spending more money on disaster planning, so that communities will be better prepared for future storms. Advances in technologies used to track hurricanes such as satellites, drones, ships, and buoys, also help areas prepare by providing advance notice of approaching storms.

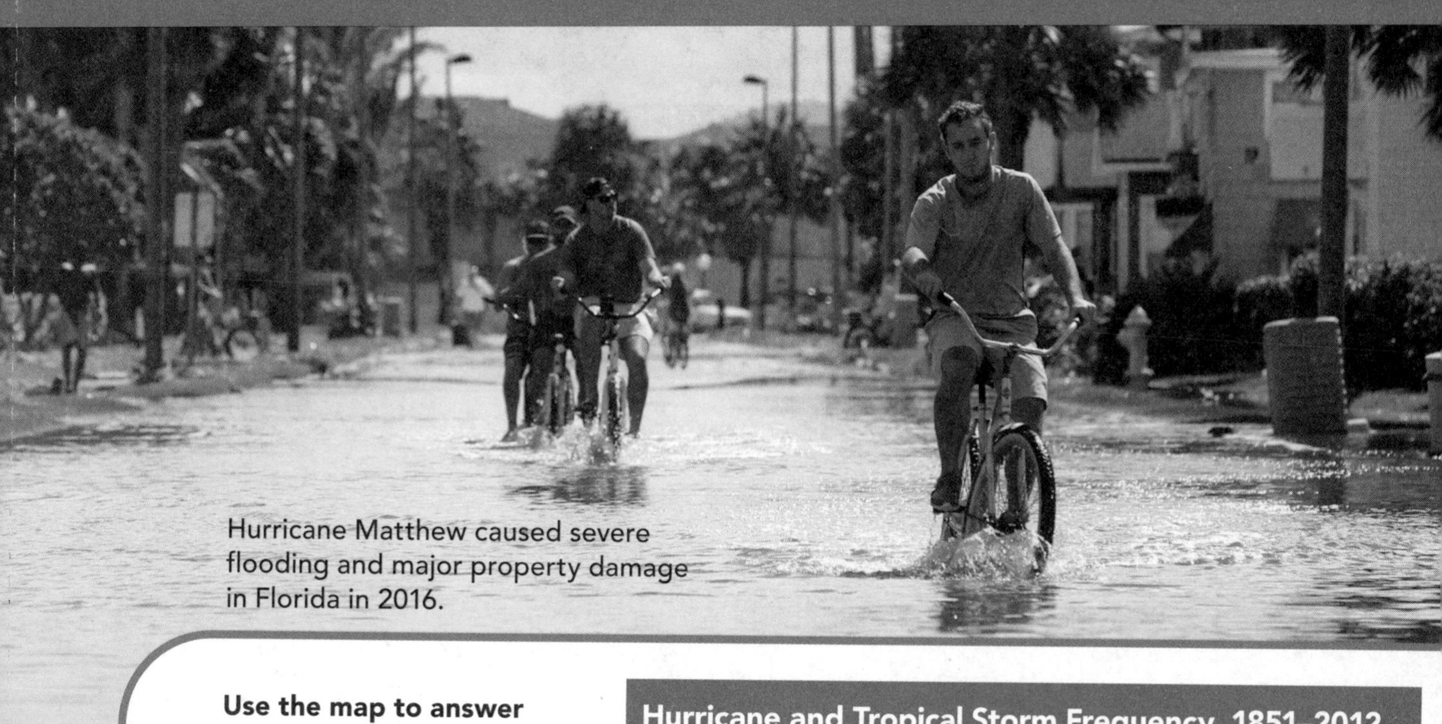

Hurricane Matthew caused severe flooding and major property damage in Florida in 2016.

Use the map to answer questions 1–2.

Hurricane and Tropical Storm Frequency, 1851–2012

KEY
65–141
29–64
1–28
No hurricanes

Source: FEMA

1. **SEP Analyze Data** What general conclusion can you reach about hurricane risk in the U.S.?

....

....

....

....

....

....

2. **SEP Construct Explanations** How would you characterize the risk of a hurricane strike where you live? Use evidence from the map to support your explanation.

....

....

3. **SEP Design Solutions** Besides the solutions mentioned in the text, what do you think people living in areas where hurricanes are common might do to address the continual threat of major hurricanes?

....

....

....

Take Notes

Use this space for recording notes and sketching out ideas.

Revisit the Anchoring Phenomenon

Conduct an Investigation

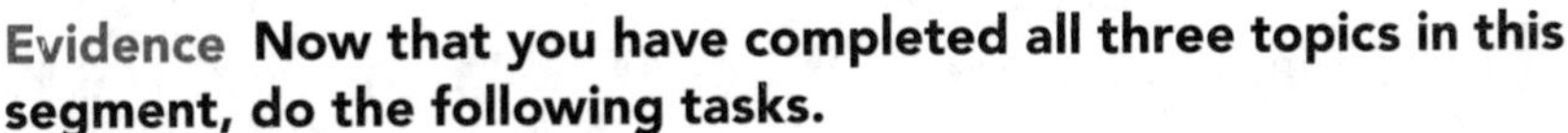

Evidence Now that you have completed all three topics in this segment, do the following tasks.

Collaborative Conversations With a partner, discuss what you have learned in this segment and how it relates to the California Floristic Province. Then, develop and expand the graphic organizer below to include evidence from this segment that helps to explain how natural processes and human activities impact biodiversity and ecosystem services in the province.

Research an Endemic Species

Case Study Now that you have identified evidence that helps to explain how natural processes and human activities impact biodiversity and ecosystem services in the California Floristic Province, you will take a closer look at how those factors affect a specific species. There are many species that exist only in California and nowhere else in the world. These endemic species are often the focus of conservation efforts within the California Floristic Province.

To learn more about the endemic species found in the California Floristic Province and what actions are being taken to preserve them, identify a specific species you want to learn more about. It could be a plant, mammal, bird, reptile, amphibian, or freshwater fish.

Now research your chosen species to learn more about it. You will want to identify and learn about the ecosystem the species lives in. You will also need to consider how natural processes, such as plate tectonics and erosion, have impacted the ecosystem and the species over time. It will also be important to investigate how human activities have impacted the ecosystem and the species. Use your completed graphic organizer as a guide for your research regarding the impact of natural processes and human activities on your species. Finally, identify any actions that have been put in place to protect your species.

These organisms are examples of endemic organisms found within the California Floristic Province.

San Francisco garter snake

San Joaquin kit fox

Revisit the Anchoring Phenomenon

Communicate a Solution

Based on your research, answer the following questions.

1. **SEP Communicate Information** Describe the species you researched and the ecosystem it lives in.

2. **CCC Stability and Change** What natural processes impact this ecosystem? Explain how your species is affected.

3. **CCC Cause and Effect** What human activities affect this ecosystem? Explain how your species is affected.

4. **SEP Construct Explanations** At the beginning of this segment, you made a claim about the impact of natural processes and human activity on biodiversity and ecosystem services in the California Floristic Province. Using evidence from the segment and your research, explain how the evidence supports your claim.

APPENDIX A

Safety Symbols

These symbols warn of possible dangers in the laboratory and remind you to work carefully.

Safety Goggles Wear safety goggles to protect your eyes in any activity involving chemicals, flames or heating, or glassware.

Lab Apron Wear a laboratory apron to protect your skin and clothing from damage.

Breakage Handle breakable materials, such as glassware, with care. Do not touch broken glassware.

Heat-Resistant Gloves Use an oven mitt or other hand protection when handling hot materials, such as hot plates or hot glassware.

Plastic Gloves Wear disposable plastic gloves when working with harmful chemicals and organisms. Keep your hands away from your face, and dispose of the gloves according to your teacher's instructions.

Heating Use a clamp or tongs to pick up hot glassware. Do not touch hot objects with your bare hands.

Flames Before you work with flames, tie back loose hair and clothing. Follow your teacher's instructions about lighting and extinguishing flames.

No Flames When using flammable materials, make sure there are no flames, sparks, or other exposed heat sources present.

Corrosive Chemical Avoid getting acid or other corrosive chemicals on your skin or clothing or in your eyes. Do not inhale the vapors. Wash your hands after the activity.

Poison Do not let any poisonous chemical come into contact with your skin, and do not inhale its vapors. Wash your hands when you are finished with the activity.

Fumes Work in a well-ventilated area when harmful vapors may be involved. Avoid inhaling vapors directly. Test an odor only when directed to do so by your teacher, and use a wafting motion to direct the vapor toward your nose.

Sharp Object Scissors, scalpels, knives, needles, pins, and tacks can cut your skin. Always direct a sharp edge or point away from yourself and others.

Animal Safety Treat live or preserved animals or animal parts with care to avoid harming the animals or yourself. Wash your hands when you are finished with the activity.

Plant Safety Handle plants only as directed by your teacher. If you are allergic to certain plants, tell your teacher; do not do an activity involving those plants. Avoid touching harmful plants such as poison ivy. Wash your hands when you are finished with the activity.

Electric Shock To avoid electric shock, never use electrical equipment around water, when the equipment is wet, or when your hands are wet. Be sure cords are untangled and cannot trip anyone. Unplug equipment not in use.

Physical Safety When an experiment involves physical activity, avoid injuring yourself or others. Alert your teacher if there is any reason you should not participate.

Disposal Dispose of chemicals and other laboratory materials safely. Follow the instructions from your teacher.

Hand Washing Wash your hands thoroughly when finished with an activity. Use soap and warm water. Rinse well.

General Safety Awareness When this symbol appears, follow the instructions provided. When you are asked to develop your own procedure in a lab, have your teacher approve your plan.

Take Notes

Use this space for recording notes and sketching out ideas.

GLOSSARY

A

abiotic factor A nonliving part of an organism's habitat.

alluvial fan A wide, sloping deposit of sediment formed where a stream leaves a mountain range.

atom The basic unit from which all matter is made.

autotroph An organism that is able to capture energy from sunlight or chemicals and use it to produce its own food.

B

biodiversity The number and variety of different species in an area.

biotic factor A living or once living part of an organism's habitat.

boiling point The temperature at which a liquid boils.

C

cellular respiration The process in which oxygen and glucose undergo a complex series of chemical reactions inside cells, releasing energy.

chemical change A change in which one or more substances combine or break apart to form new substances.

chemical property A characteristic of a substance that describes its ability to change into different substances.

chemical weathering The process that breaks down rock through chemical changes.

chlorophyll A green photosynthetic pigment found in the chloroplasts of plants, algae, and some bacteria.

closed system A system in which no matter is allowed to enter or leave.

commensalism A type of symbiosis between two species in which one species benefits and the other species is neither helped nor harmed.

community All the different populations that live together in a certain area.

competition The struggle between organisms to survive as they attempt to use the same limited resources in the same place at the same time.

compound A substance made of two or more elements chemicallly combined in a specific ration, or proportion.

compression Stress that squeezes rock until it folds or breaks.

condensation The change in state from a gas to a liquid.

conservation The practice of using less of a resource so that it can last longer.

consumer An organism that obtains energy by feeding on other organisms.

continental glacier A glacier that covers much of a continent or large island.

convergent boundary A plate boundary where two plates move toward each other.

crust The layer of rock that forms Earth's outer surface.

crystal A solid in which the atoms are arranged in a pattern that repeats again and again.

crystallization The process by which atoms are arranged to form a material with a crystal structure.

crystallize To form a crystal structure.

D

decomposer An organism that gets energy by breaking down biotic wastes and dead organisms and returns raw materials to the soil and water.

deflation The process by which wind removes surface materials.

delta A landform made of sediment that is deposited where a river flows into an ocean or lake.

density The measurement of how much mass of a substance is contained in a given volume.

deposition Process in which sediment is laid down in new locations.

desalination A process that removes salt from sea water to make fresh water.

divergent boundary A plate boundary where two plates move away from each other.

dormant Term used to describe a volcano that is not currently acrtive but able to become active in the future.

drought A long period of low precipitation.

E

earthquake The shaking that results from the movement of rock beneath Earth's surface.

ecological restoration The practice of helping a degraded or destroyed ecosystem recover from damage.

ecology The study of how organisms interact with each other and their environment.

ecosystem The community of organisms that live in a particular area, along with their nonliving environment.

ecosystem services The benefits that humans derive from ecosystems.

element A pure substance that cannot be broken down into other substances by chemical or physical means.

energy pyramid A diagram that shows the amount of energy that moves from one feeding level to another in a food web.

erosion The process by which water, ice, wind, or gravity moves weathered particles of rock and soil.

evaporation The process by which molecules at the surface of a liquid absorb enough energy to change to a gas.

extinct volcano Term used to describe a volcano that is no longer active and unlikely to erupt again

extinction The disappearance of all members of a species from Earth.

F

fault A break in Earth's crust along which rocks move.

fermentation The process by which cells release energy by breaking down food molecules without using oxygen.

flood An overflowing of water in a normally dry area.

flood plain The flat, wide area of land along a river.

food chain A series of events in an ecosystem in which organisms transfer energy by eating and by being eaten.

food web The pattern of overlapping feeding relationships or food chains among the various organisms in an ecosystem.

fossil fuel Energy-rich substance formed from the remains of organisms.

freezing point The temperature at which a liquid freezes.

G

gas A state of matter with no definite shape or volume.

glacier Any large mass of ice that moves slowly over land.

groundwater Water that fills the cracks and spaces in underground soil and rock layers.

H

habitat An environment that provides the things a specific organism needs to live, grow, and reproduce.

heterotroph An organism that cannot make its own food and gets food by consuming other living things.

hot spot An area where magma from deep within the mantle melts through the crust above it.

humus Dark-colored organic material in soil.

hurricane A tropical storm that has winds of about 119 kilometers per hour or higher.

I

ice age Time in Earth's history during which glaciers covered large parts of the surface.

igneous rock A type of rock that forms from the cooling of molten rock at or below the surface.

inner core A dense sphere of solid iron and nickel at the center of Earth.

invasive species Species that are not native to a habitat and can out-compete native species in an ecosystem.

K

keystone species A species that influences the survival of many other species in an ecosystem.

L

lava Liquid magma that reaches the surface.

limiting factor An environmental factor that causes a population to decrease in size.

liquid A state of matter that has no definite shape but has a definite volume.

loess A wind-formed deposit made of fine particles of clay and silt.

longshore drift The movement of water and sediment down a beach caused by waves coming in to shore at an angle.

M

magma A molten mixture of rock-forming substances, gases, and water from the mantle.

magnitude The measurement of an earthquake's strength based on seismic waves and movement along faults.

mantle The layer of hot, solid material between Earth's crust and core.

mass A measure of how much matter is in an object.

mass movement Any one of several processes by which gravity moves sediment downhill.

matter Anything that has mass and takes up space.

mechanical weathering The type of weathering in which rock is physically broken into smaller pieces.

melting point The temperature at which a substance changes from a solid to a liquid; the same as the freezing point, or temperature at which a liquid changes to a solid.

metamorphic rock A type of rock that forms from an existing rock that is changed by heat, pressure, or chemical reactions.

mid-ocean ridge An undersea mountain chain where new ocean floor is produced; a divergent plate boundary under the ocean.

mineral A naturally occurring solid that can form by inorganic processes and that has a crystal structure and a definite chemical composition.

mixture Two or more substances that are together in the same place, but their atoms are not chemically bonded.

molecule A group of two or more atoms held together by chemical bonds.

mutualism A type of symbiosis in which both species benefit from living together.

N

natural resource Anything naturally occurring in the environment that humans use.

nonrenewable resource A natural resource that is not replaced in a useful time frame.

nuclear fission The splitting of an atom's nuclues into two nuclei, which releases a great deal of energy.

O

ocean trench An undersea valley that represents one of the deepest parts of the ocean.

open system A system in which matter can enter from or escape to the surroundings.

ore A mineral deposit large enough and valuable enough for it to be extracted from the ground.

organism A living thing.

outer core A layer of molten iron and nickel that surrounds the inner core of Earth.

P

parasitism A type of symbiosis in which one organism lives with, on, or in a host and harms it.

petroleum Liquid fossil fuel; oil.

photosynthesis The process by which plants and other autotrophs capture and use light energy to make food from carbon dioxide and water.

physical change A change that alters the form or appearance of a material but does not make the material into another substance.

physical property A characteristic of a pure substance that can be observed without changing it into another substance.

pioneer species The first species to populate an area during succession.

plucking The process by which a glacier picks up rocks as it flows over the land.

polymer A long chain of molecules made up of repeating units.

population All the members of one species living in the same area.

precipitation Any form of water that falls from clouds and reaches Earth's surface as rain, snow, sleet, or hail.

predation An interaction in which one organism kills another for food or nutrients.

producer An organism that can make its own food.

product A substance formed as a result of a chemical reaction.

R

reactant A substance that enters into a chemical reaction.

rock cycle A series of processes on the surface and inside Earth that slowly changes rocks from one kind to another.

runoff Water that flows over the ground surface rather than soaking into the ground.

S

sand dune A deposit of wind-blown sand.

sea-floor spreading The process by which molten material adds new oceanic crust to the ocean floor.

sediment Small, solid pieces of material that come from rocks or the remains of organisms; earth materials deposited by erosion.

sedimentary rock A type of rock that forms when particles from other rocks or the remains of plants and animals are pressed and cemented together.

seismic wave Vibrations that travel through Earth carrying the energy released during an earthquake.

shearing Stress that pushes masses of rock in opposite directions, in a sideways movement.

soil The loose, weathered material on Earth's surface in which plants can grow.

solid A state of matter that has a definite shape and a definite volume.

solubility A measure of how much a substance dissolves in another substance.

storm A violent disturbance in the atmosphere.

storm surge A "dome" of water that sweeps across the coast where a hurricane lands.

stream A channel through which water is continually flowing downhill.

stress A force that acts on rock to change its shape or volume.

subduction The process by which oceanic crust sinks beneath a deep-ocean trench and back into the mantle at a convergent plate boundary.

sublimation The change in state from a solid directly to a gas without passing through the liquid state.

substance A single kind of matter that is pure and has a specific set of properties.

succession The series of predictable changes that occur in a community over time.

sustainability The ability of an ecosystem to maintain bioviersity and production indefinitely.

symbiosis Any relationship in which two species live closely together and that benefits at least one of the species.

synthetic Created or manufactured by humans; not found occurring in nature

T

temperature How hot or cold something is; a measure of the average energy of motion of the particles of a substance; the measure of the average kinetic energy of the particles of a substance.

tension Stress that stretches rock so that it becomes thinner in the middle.

thermal energy The total kinetic and potential energy of all the particles of an object.

thunderstorm A small storm often accompanied by heavy precipitation and frequent thunder and lightning.

till The sediments deposited directly by a glacier.

tornado A rapidly whirling, funnel-shaped cloud that reaches down to touch Earth's surface.

transform boundary A plate boundary where two plates move past each other in opposite directions.

tributary A stream or river that flows into a larger river.

tsunami A giant wave usually caused by an earthquake beneath the ocean floor.

U

uniformitarianism The geologic principle that the same geologic processes that operate today operated in the past to change Earth's surface.

V

valley glacier A long, narrow glacier that forms when snow and ice build up in a mountain valley.

vaporization The change of state from a liquid to a gas.

volcano A weak spot in the crust where magma has come to the surface.

volume The amount of space that matter occupies.

W

weight A measure of the force of gravity acting on an object.

INDEX

Page number in **Bold** are vocabulary terms. *Italic* page numbers are of charts, graphs, pictures, and features.

A

B

C

INDEX

Page number in **Bold** are vocabulary terms. *Italic* page numbers are of charts, graphs, pictures, and features.

D

E

F

G

I

L

M

INDEX

Page number in **Bold** are vocabulary terms. *Italic* page numbers are of charts, graphs, pictures, and features.

S

T

INDEX

Page number in **Bold** are vocabulary terms. *Italic* page numbers are of charts, graphs, pictures, and features.

CREDITS

Photography

Photo locators denoted as follows: Top (T), Center (C), Bottom (B), Left (L), Right (R), Background (Bkgd)

Covers

Front: Casey Kiernan/Moment/Getty Images; Meganopierson/Shutterstock; Zoonar GmbH/Alamy Stock Photo; Stocktrek Images, Inc./Alamy Stock Photo; Back: Marinello/DigitalVision Vectors/Getty Images

Instructional Segment 4

iv: Nick Lundgren/Shutterstock; vi: Gary Crabbe/AGE Fotostock; vii: Robert Harding/Alamy Stock Photo viii: Kong Act/Shutterstock; x: Fabriziobalconi/Fotolia; xBkgd: Brian J. Skerry/National Geographic/Getty Images; xi: Dale Kolke/ZUMA Press/Newscom; xii: Sarah Fields Photography/Shutterstock; xiiCL: Ronnie Gregory/EyeEm/Getty Images; xiiCR: Peter Essick/Aurora Photos/Alamy Stock Photo; 002: Westend61/Getty Images; 004CL: Ronnie Gregory/EyeEm/Getty Images; 004CR: Peter Essick/Aurora Photos/Alamy Stock Photo; 004BR: Sarah Fields Photography/Shutterstock; 005: Mike Flippo/Shutterstock; 006BL: David Courtenay/Getty Images; 006BR: Mark Ralston/AFP/Getty Images; 008: Gary Crabbe/AGE Fotostock; 010: Christopher Boswell/Shutterstock; 017TL: Mr. Elliot Lim and Mr. Jesse Varner, CIRES & NOAA/NCEI; 017TR: OAR/National Undersea Research Program/NOAA; 021: Sueddeutsche Zeitung Photo/Alamy Stock Photo; 022: MarkushaBLR/Fotolia; 028: Ed Burns/EyeEm/Getty Images; 029CR: David Burton/Alamy Stock Photo; 029B: Vadim Petrakov/Shutterstock; 032: The Asahi Shimbun/Getty Images; 036: Tom Uhlman/Alamy Stock Photo; 041: JIJI PRESS/AFP/Getty Images; 043: Nat Farbman/ The LIFE Images Collection/Getty Images; 044: Pall Gudonsson/Getty Images; 050TL: Siim Sepp/Alamy Stock Photo; 050TR: Sandatlas/Shutterstock; 051: Hulton Archive/Getty Images; 052TL: Janet Babb/Hawaiian Volcano Observatory/U.S. Geological Survey; 052BR: Rosa Irene Betancourt 3/Alamy Stock Photo; 057: Space_Expert/Fotolia; 060: Robert Harding/Alamy Stock Photo; 062: Maggie Steber/Getty Images; 063: Xu Jian/Getty Images; 064: ImageBROKER/Alamy Stock Photo; 066TL: Sean Kaufmann/Getty Images; 066TR: Thomas Mitchell/Alamy Stock Photo; 067TC: Mironov/Shutterstock; 067TL: IPics Photography/Alamy Stock Photo; 069: Madllen/123RF; 071TCR: Sean Kaufmann/Getty Images; 071TR: Vinicius Tupinamba/Shutterstock; 073: Alejandro Zepeda/Newscom; 081TR: Roman Kadarjan/Alamy Stock Photo; 081B: David Weintraub/Science Source; 082: Richard Cummins/Getty Images; 087TL: Planet Observer/UIG/Getty Images; 087CL: Totajla/Shutterstock; 089: Macduff Everton/Getty Images; 090: AP Images; 092: Design Pics Inc/Alamy Stock Photo; 099: INTERFOTO/Alamy Stock Photo; 102: Smith Collection/Gado/Getty Images; 105: Stnazkul/123RF; 108: Carlo Allegri/Reuters; 109: Noah Berger/AFP/Getty Images; 115: Mick Jack/Alamy Stock Photo; 118: Kong Act/Shutterstock; 120: Skyward Kick Productions/Shutterstock; 122: All Canada Photos/Alamy Stock Photo; 124: Frank Slack/Moment Open/Getty Images; 125TC: Chloe Kaudeur/EyeEm/Getty Images; 125TCR: Russell Burden/Stockbyte/Getty Images; 125TL: Alessio Frizziero/EyeEm/Getty Images; 125TR: Steve Leach/Moment Open/Getty Images; 126: George Wilhelm/Los Angeles Times/Getty Images; 128: Dorling Kindersley/Getty Images; 129TR: Ktsdesign/Shutterstock; 129CL: Bryan Knox/Papilio/Alamy Stock Photo; 129BR: Shaen Adey/Gallo Images ROOTS Collection/Getty Images; 130BL: WaterFrame/Alamy Stock Photo; 130BR: Stephen Bonk/Fotolia; 132: Erich Schmidt/imageBROKER/Getty Images; 134: Rich Pedroncelli/AP Images; 138: Pete Fickenscher/NOAA/NWS/WR/RFC Sacramento; 139: Tony Campbell/Shutterstock; 140: Elvis Antson/Shutterstock; 142: George Rose/Getty Images; 143: Ludmila Yilmaz/Shutterstock; 144: Frieda Ryckaert/Getty Images; 145: Adria Photography/Getty Images; 146: 2630ben/Shutterstock; 147Bkgd: Charles Knowles/Shutterstock; 147TL: Georgy Rozov/EyeEm Creative/Getty Images; 147TR: William Silver/Shutterstock; 147CL: Zeljko Radojko/Shutterstock; 147CR: VCG/Getty Images; 147BR: Zhai Jianlan/Xinhua/Alamy Stock Photo; 148T: Reinhard Dirscherl/Alamy Stock Photo; 148B: Stocktrek Images, Inc/Alamy Stock Photo; 149CR: Ariel Skelley/Getty Images; 149BL: Michael Doolittle/Alamy Stock Photo; 149BR: Goodluz/Shutterstock; 150: Roberto Nistri/Alamy Stock Photo; 152: Design Pics Inc/Alamy Stock Photo; 153: 123RF; 154BC: Holbox/Shutterstock; 154BL: Ammit Jack/Shutterstock; 154BR: Kletr/Shutterstock; 154C: Mathew Spolin/Getty Images; 154CL: Hero Images/Getty Images; 154CR: Pink Candy/Shutterstock; 155: Melpomene/Shutterstock; 157: Pawe/Shutterstock; 158: Nik Wheeler/Alamy Stock Photo; 159: Michael Willis/Alamy Stock Photo; 161T: Commission Air/Alamy Stock Photo; 161B: Michael Willis/Alamy Stock Photo; 165T: Jose A. Bernat Bacete/Moment Open/Getty Images; 165BR: Redmal/E+/Getty Images; 174BL: Suzanne L and Joseph T. Collins/Getty Images; 174BR: Kevin Schafer/Nature Picture Library; 180BL: Suzanne L and Joseph T. Collins/Getty Images; 180BR: Kevin Schafer/Nature Picture Library.

Take Notes

Use this space for recording notes and sketching out ideas.

Take Notes

Use this space for recording notes and sketching out ideas.

Take Notes

Use this space for recording notes and sketching out ideas.

Take Notes

Use this space for recording notes and sketching out ideas.

Take Notes

Use this space for recording notes and sketching out ideas.

Take Notes

Use this space for recording notes and sketching out ideas.

Take Notes

Use this space for recording notes and sketching out ideas.